man's funniest friend

Also selected and edited by William Cole

BEASTLY BOYS AND GHASTLY GIRLS

THE BIRDS AND THE BEASTS WERE THERE

POEMS FOR SEASONS AND CELEBRATIONS

POEMS OF MAGIC AND SPELLS

I WENT TO THE ANIMAL FAIR

STORY POEMS NEW AND OLD

HUMOROUS POETRY FOR CHILDREN

man's funniest friend

friend

THE IN STORIES
REMINISCENCES
POEMS AND CARTOONS

SELECTED AND EDITED BY

william cole

THE WORLD PUBLISHING COMPANY

cleveland and new york

Published by The World Publishing Company
2231 West 110th Street, Cleveland, Ohio 44102
Library of Congress catalog card number: 67-23352
Copyright © 1967 by William Cole

H L

Designed by Jack Jaget

COPYRIGHT ACKNOWLEDGMENTS

The editor and The World Publishing Company herewith render thanks to the following authors, publishers, and agents whose interest, co-operation, and permission to reprint have made possible the preparation of Man's Funniest Friend: The Dog in Stories, Reminiscences, Poems, and Cartoons. *All possible care has been taken to trace the ownership of every selection included and to make full acknowledgment for its use. If any errors have accidentally occurred, they will be corrected in subsequent editions, provided notification is sent to the publishers.*

The American Legion Magazine and John Gallagher, for one cartoon by John Gallagher. Reprinted by permission of *The American Legion Magazine* and John Gallagher.

Roger Angell, for "Living With a Dog," copyright 1951 by Roger Angell. Originally published in *Holiday* magazine. Reprinted by permission of Roger Angell.

Angus & Robertson, Ltd., and Lansdowne Press, for "Making Money Out of Dogs: A Tale of the Great Depression" by Len Lower from *Modern Australian Humour*, edited by Bill Wanna. Reprinted by permission of Angus & Robertson, Ltd., and Lansdowne Press.

Ashley Famous Agency, Inc., for "Mad Dogs and Englishmen" from *The Day of the Dog* by Michael Frayn, copyright 1962 by Michael Frayn. Reprinted by permission of Ashley Famous Agency, Inc.

The Bodley Head, Ltd., for "Once Bitten" from *Next to Oddliness* by Paul Jennings, copyright 1955 by Max Reinhardt, Ltd. Reprinted by permission of The Bodley Head, Ltd.

Curtis Brown, Ltd., for "A Dog's Best Friend Is His Illiteracy" by Ogden Nash, copyright 1949 by The Curtis Publishing Company; for "Flurry at the Sheep Dog Trial" from *Sam Small Flies Again* by Eric Knight, copyright 1937 by Eric Knight. Renewal, 1965, by Jere Knight. Reprinted by permission of Curtis Brown, Ltd.

Diogenes Verlag, for six cartoons from *Auf Den Hund Gekommen* by Loriot. Reprinted by permission of Diogenes Verlag, Zurich, Switzerland.

Doubleday & Company, Inc., for "Dogs That Have Known Me" from *Please Don't Eat the Daisies* by Jean Kerr, copyright 1957 by Condé Nast Publications; for "The Radical Flea" from *The Lives and Times of Archy and Mehitabel* by Don Marquis, copyright 1935 by Doubleday & Company, Inc. Reprinted by permission of Doubleday & Company, Inc.

E. P. Dutton & Company, Inc., for illustrations from *Top Dog*, written and illustrated by Norman Thelwell, copyright 1962, 1963, 1964 by Norman Thelwell and Beaverbrook Newspapers, Ltd. Reprinted by permission of E. P. Dutton & Company, Inc.

Elliott Erwitt, for the use of his photographs.

Fawcett World Library, for one cartoon by Dumas which appeared in *True;* for one cartoon by Virgil Partch which appeared in *Cartoon Fun*. Reprinted by permission of *True*, The Man's Magazine.

The Stephen Greene Press, for seven cartoons by Larry from *Man's Best Friend*, copyright 1966 by Terence Parkes. Reprinted by permission of The Stephen Greene Press.

Harper & Row, Publishers, Inc., for "Your Boy and His Dog" from *Chips Off the Old Benchley* by Robert Benchley, copyright 1932 by The Hearst Corporation, New York Mirror Division; for "The Low State of Whippet Racing" from *Inside Benchley* by Robert Benchley, with illustrations by Gluyas Williams, copyright 1928 by Harper & Brothers; for "Dogs and Public Service" from *From Bed to Worse* by Robert Benchley, with illustrations by Gluyas Williams, copyright 1934 by Robert C. Benchley; for "Fashions in Dogs" from *The Fox of Peapack and Other Poems* by E. B. White, copyright 1936, 1964 by E. B. White. Originally appeared in *The New Yorker;* for "Sunning" from *A World To Know* by James S. Tippett, copyright 1933 by Harper & Brothers. Renewal, 1961, by Martha K. Tippett. Reprinted by permission of Harper & Row, Publishers, Inc.

Margaret Held, for one illustration by John Held, Jr.

Houghton Mifflin Company, for "The Dog Who Paid Cash" by Will Rogers from *The Autobiography of Will Rogers*, edited by Donald Day. Reprinted by permission of Houghton Mifflin Company.

Little, Brown and Company, for "The Dog" from *Everyone But Thee and Me* by Ogden Nash, copyright 1962 by Ogden Nash. Reprinted by permission of Little, Brown and Company; for "Canine Cuisine" from *The Parables of Peter Partout* by John Gould, illustrated by F. Wenderoth Saunders, text copyright 1964 by John T. Gould, illustrations copyright 1964 by F. Wenderoth Saunders. Reprinted by permission of the author and Little, Brown and Company; for "Dog" from *Boy Blue's Book of Beasts* by William Jay Smith, copyright 1956, 1957 by William Jay Smith. Reprinted by permission of Atlantic-Little, Brown and Company.

The Macmillan Company, for "The Way Old Tige Barked" from *Folk Laughter on the American Frontier* by Mody C. Boatright, copyright 1949 by Mody C. Boatright; for three drawings from *Max Presents* by Pericle Luigi Giovannetti, copyright 1954 by Pericle Luigi Giovannetti. Reprinted by permission of The Macmillan Company.

Magnum Photos, Inc., and Elliott Erwitt, for one photograph by Elliott Erwitt.

The Harold Matson Company, Inc., for "Butch and the Lark" from *The World, the Flesh and H. Allen Smith* by H. Allen Smith, copyright 1953 by H. Allen Smith. Reprinted by permission of The Harold Matson Company, Inc.

Newspaper Enterprise Association, for two cartoons from *Out Our Way* by J. R. Williams. Reprinted by permission of Newspaper Enterprise Association.

S. J. Perelman and The New Yorker Magazine, Inc., for "The Slicker the Vet, the Sicker the Pet" from *The Rising Gorge* by S. J. Perelman, copyright 1960 by The New Yorker Magazine, Inc. Reprinted by permission of The New Yorker Magazine, Inc.

Prentice-Hall, Inc., for *How To Live With a Neurotic Dog* by Stephen Baker, with illustrations by Eric Gurney, copyright 1960 by Prentice-Hall, Inc. Reprinted by permission of Prentice-Hall, Inc.

The Ben Roth Agency, Inc., for cartoons from *Punch;* for "Ascension and Declination of Sirius" by Colin Howard; for "Something of a Borzoi" by D. D. Porter; for "The Deaf Adder" by Colin Howard; for "The Swimming Lesson" by Arthur P. Jacobs. All originally published in *Punch,* copyright Punch Publications, Ltd. Reprinted by permission of The Ben Roth Agency, Inc., and Punch Publications, Ltd.

The Saturday Evening Post and John Gallagher, for three cartoons, copyright 1957 by The Curtis Publishing Company, copyright 1953 by The Curtis Publishing Company, copyright 1964 by The Curtis Publishing Company. Reprinted by permission of *The Saturday Evening Post* and John Gallagher.

The Saturday Evening Post and Henry Syverson, for three cartoons, copyright 1948 by The Curtis Publishing Company, copyright 1958 by The Curtis Publishing Company, copyright 1963 by The Curtis Publishing Company. Reprinted by permission of *The Saturday Evening Post* and Henry Syverson.

A. B. Sens, for one cartoon which appeared in *Evergreen Review*. Reprinted by permission of A. B. Sens.

Simon & Schuster, Inc., for two cartoons from *The Dog* by Roy McKie, copyright 1954 by Roy McKie. Reprinted by permission of Simon & Schuster, Inc.

Neville Spearman, Ltd., for one illustration by Sprod from *The Best Humour From Punch,* edited by William Cole, copyright by Neville Spearman, Ltd. Reprinted by permission of Neville Spearman, Ltd.

William Steig and The New Yorker Magazine, Inc., for four drawings by William Steig, copyright 1965 by The New Yorker Magazine, Inc., copyright 1966 by The New Yorker Magazine, Inc., copyright 1967 by The New Yorker Magazine, Inc. Reprinted by permission of William Steig and The New Yorker Magazine, Inc.

Tetsu and McKee and Mouche for two cartoons.

This Week magazine and John Gallagher, for one cartoon by John Gallagher, copyright 1956 by the United Newspapers Magazine Corporation. Reprinted by permission of *This Week* magazine and John Gallagher.

Helen Thurber, for "The Dog That Bit People" from *My Life and Hard Times* by James Thurber, published by Harper & Row, copyright 1933 by James Thurber. Renewal, 1961, by James Thurber; for "Canines in the Cellar" from *Thurber's Dogs* by James Thurber, published by Simon & Schuster, copyright 1955 by James Thurber. Originally published in *The New Yorker;* for one cartoon and a drawing from *Thurber and Company* by James Thurber, published by Harper & Row, copyright 1966 by Helen Thurber; for one cartoon from *Men, Women and Dogs,* published by Harcourt, Brace and World, copyright 1943 by James Thurber. Originally published in *The New Yorker*. Reprinted by permission of Helen Thurber.

P. G. Wodehouse and Scott Meredith Literary Agency, Inc., for "The Go-Getter" from *Blandings Castle* by P. G. Wodehouse, copyright 1924, 1926, 1927, 1928, 1931, 1932, 1933, 1935, 1952, 1954, 1955, 1956, 1959, 1960, 1961, 1963 by Pelham Grenville Wodehouse. Reprinted by permission of P. G. Wodehouse and his agents, Scott Meredith Literary Agency, Inc.

The World Journal Tribune, for one cartoon by Clare Briggs. Reprinted by permission of the New York *World Journal Tribune*.

Ralph Wotherspoon, for his poem "Our Dumb Friends."

contents

introduction

I know a man who barks at dogs. He's Elliott Erwitt, whose dog photographs are in this book. Whenever he comes upon a dog in the street he pauses, leans over slightly toward the animal, and gives a loud "rowf!" Reactions vary. Dogs don't expect their two-footed friends to bark; some get extremely jittery, some bark back, some simply look stunned. If there is a human on the other end of the leash, *his* annoyance is usually expressed in "a few well-chosen words." But frequently, Mr. Erwitt reports, the dogs seem to enjoy the situation, and a rapport is established between the barkers.

Despite the recent rash of books about brilliant otters and scintillating sloths, dogs remain the only animals who communicate happily with man. Cats are aloof and disdainful, out for what they can get; horses are—let's face it—stupid. Pigs? Yes, pigs are intelligent, certainly, but they don't make particularly good pets. Dogs are fun to be with; they're unwitting comics—and what's more I sometimes even believe that dogs have a sense of humor. Samuel Butler said, "The great pleasure of a dog is that you may make a fool of yourself with him and not only will he not scold you, but he will make a fool of himself too." How often we wish our human friends were like that!

11

I don't go along with James Thurber's famous remark that "a dog-lover is a dog in love with another dog." He was putting us on, and being over-finicky about the language. There are human dog lovers too. Of course none of us can love *all* dogs indiscriminately. If you've ever been to a dog show, where a thousand dogs are massed together, you'll see some that not even a mother dog could love. From my last dog show I remember a terrifying Doberman snarling and frothing at every creature in sight, a chow chow acting for all the world as snuffy as a cat, and a bunch of those shivery-legged, pop-eyed teeny dogs—I can't go for those. Then again, no dogs are at their best chained to a stall or cramped in a wire cage at a dog show: the Irish setters were nervous wrecks, the whippets bore looks of pitiable resignation, the bullterriers were big show-offs barking at passing dogs while simultaneously wagging their tails, the ghostly Weimaraners looked at you with sad yellow eyes, the French poodles were obviously embarrassed to be seen in public wearing their curlers. The Basenji wore tiny wrinkled frowns, but they were the only breed that made no vocal complaints. I complimented their owner on this. "That's right," he said, "they haven't any voice."

The dogs you meet at a dog show are all purebred dogs, naturally, and I'm sure there are good guys and bad guys among them. I've never had much to do with purebreds; as a boy I had the usual succession of dogs, but they were all of them mutts. ("Mutt," the dictionary says, is "probably shortened from *muttonhead*," which seems to me to be grossly unfair.) As an adult I move around quite a bit, and live in the heart of the city, which means that I haven't been able to keep a dog. As a result, I'm dog-starved; if I go visiting where there's a dog, I'm frequently accused of spending more time talking to the dog than to the hosts, and of romping about with the dog rather than with the children. I sometimes borrow a dog for a weekend or longer. One recent summer when I lived by the seashore, I borrowed Lola, a dog with a bottomless stomach and an undecipherable ancestry. Lola was not exactly brilliant, but she was pretty, friendly, and funny. Her only annoying idiosyncrasy was that her sense of property was too strong. She wanted to mangle any stranger dog who so much as stepped on a blade of my grass. She wasn't big, but she had a powerful sense of righteous indignation. A typical incident: I was standing by the window overlooking the road that passed my house; along came an old, old man with a cane, accompanied by an old, old police dog and a small granddaughter. Lola, who'd been snoozing in a large hole she'd dug for herself in the lawn, looked up and saw a stranger dog on the verge of my property. Well! The ensuing scene was certainly spirited; I came dashing out of the house shouting, "Lola! Lola! No! No!" and the old man was yelling and lashing about with his cane like a demented musketeer, the dogs were snarling, snapping, going head over heels on the roadway, up, down; then off tore the police dog, Lola close behind, and the little girl kept shouting, "He bited Freddie's tail! He bited Freddie's tail!" This sort of thing can be wearing. But despite such shortcomings Lola was a pleasure: if you'd been away for as little as an hour she'd go into ecstasies at your return, and run around in circles at top speed. And sometimes when you'd get up in the middle of the night you'd hear the reassuring thump, thump of her tail on the floor, letting you know that she was there and thinking of you.

I am always amused when I contemplate the peculiarities of Sonia, a bullterrier my friend Richard Bissell owned years ago when he lived on a houseboat in Dubuque, Iowa. The oddest thing about Sonia was her affinity for beer bottles. First thing every morning she would pick a beer bottle up by the neck, and all day long she'd carry it with her wherever she went. People would look down at the houseboat from the bridge, exclaiming, "Lookit that crazy dog walking around with a beer bottle!" Her owner reports that once, when she was just a pup, Sonia saw a mouse in a certain corner of the living room. For many years afterward, from time to time she'd remember that something interesting once happened in that corner, so she'd station herself there for a half an hour at a stretch, looking at the baseboard, beer bottle drooping from her mouth.

In every writer's past there's a dog or two waiting to be resurrected in print, and I was happy to find that the masters of humor—James Thurber, Robert Benchley, Ogden Nash, S. J. Perelman, and P. G. Wodehouse—have all delighted in dogs. Looking through the contents of this book, I see that almost all the stories and reminiscences are concerned with the embarrassments and inconveniences of being a dog owner. But none of the writers is *really* angry—it's all make-believe. Every one is a dog lover at heart; each is *really* saying, "Dog, you're an ornery, troublesome, ludicrous, contrary, silly dumb beast— but I love you."

WILLIAM COLE

man's funniest friend

your boy and his dog

from *Chips Off the Old Benchley*

ROBERT BENCHLEY

People are constantly writing in to this department and asking: "What kind of dog shall I give my boy?" or sometimes: "What kind of boy shall I give my dog?" And although we are always somewhat surprised to get a query like this, ours really being the Jam and Fern Question Box, we usually give the same answer to both forms of inquiry: "Are you quite sure that you want to do either?" This confuses them, and we are able to snatch a few more minutes for our regular work.

But the question of Boy and Dog is one which will not be downed. There is no doubt that every healthy, normal boy (if there is such a thing in these days of Child Study) should own a dog at some time in his life, preferably between the ages of forty-five and fifty. Give a dog to a boy who is much younger and his parents will find themselves obliged to pack up and go to the Sailors' Snug Harbor to live until the dog runs away—which he will do as soon as the first pretty face comes along.

But a dog teaches a boy fidelity, perseverance, and to turn around three times before lying down—very important traits in times like these. In fact, just as soon as a dog comes along who, in addition to these qualities, also knows when to buy and sell stocks, he can be moved right up to the boy's bedroom and the boy can sleep in the dog house.

In buying a dog for a very small child, attention must be paid to one or two essential points. In the first place, the dog must not be one which will come apart easily or of such a breed that the sizing will get pasty and all gummed up when wet. Dachshunds are ideal dogs for small children, as they are already stretched and pulled to such a length that the child cannot do much harm one way or the other. The dachshund being so long also makes it difficult for a very small child to go through with the favorite juvenile maneuver of lifting the dog's hind legs up in the air and wheeling it along like a barrow, cooing, "Diddy-app!" Any small child trying to lift a dachshund's hind leg up very high is going to find itself flat on its back.

For the very small child who likes to pick animals up around the middle and carry them over to the fireplace, mastiffs, St. Bernards, or Russian wolfhounds are not indicated—that is, not if the child is of any value at all. It is not that the larger dogs resent being carried around the middle and dropped in the fireplace (in fact, the smaller the dog, the more touchy it is in matters of dignity, as is so often the case with people and nations) ; but, even though a mastiff does everything that it can to help the child in carrying it by the diaphragm, there are matters of gravity to be reckoned with which make it impossible to carry the thing through without something being broken. If a dog could be trained to wrestle and throw the child immediately, a great deal of time could be saved.

But, as we have suggested, the ideal age for a boy to own a dog is between forty-five and fifty. By this time the boy ought to have attained his full growth and, provided he is ever going to, ought to know more or less what he wants to make of himself in life. At this age the dog will be more of a companion than a chattel, and, if necessary, can be counted upon to carry the boy by the middle and drop him into bed in case sleep overcomes him at a dinner or camp meeting or anything. It can also be counted upon to tell him he has made a fool of himself and embarrassed all his friends. A wife could do no more.

The training of the dog is something which should be left to the boy, as this teaches him responsibility and accustoms him to the use of authority, probably the only time he will ever have a chance to use it. If, for example, the dog insists on following the boy when he is leaving the house, even after repeated commands to "Go on back home!" the boy must decide on one of two courses. He must either take the dog back to the house and lock it in the cellar, or, as an alternate course, he can give up the idea of going out himself and stay with the dog. The latter is the better way, especially if the dog is in good voice and given to screaming the house down.

There has always been considerable difference of opinion as to whether or not a dog really thinks. I, personally, have no doubt that distinct mental processes do go on inside the dog's brain, although many times these processes are hardly worthy of the name. I have known dogs, especially puppies, who were almost as stupid as humans in their mental reactions.

The only reason that puppies do not get into more trouble than they do (if there *is* any more trouble than that which puppies get into) is that they are so small. A child, for instance, should not expect to be able to fall as heavily, eat as heartily of shoe leather, or throw up as casually as a puppy does, for there is more bulk to a child and the results of these practices will be more serious in exact proportion to the size and capacity. Whereas, for example, a puppy might be able to eat only the toe of a slipper, a child might well succeed in eating the whole shoe—which, considering the nails and everything, would not be wise.

One of the reasons why dogs are given credit for serious thinking is the formation of their eyebrows. A dog lying in front of a fire and looking up at his master may appear pathetic, disapproving, sage, or amused, according to the angle at which its eyebrows are set by nature.

It is quite possible, and even probable, that nothing at all is going on behind the eyebrows. In fact, one dog who had a great reputation for sagacity once told me in confidence that most of the time when he was supposed to be regarding a human with an age-old philosophical rumination he was really asleep behind his shaggy overhanging brows. "You could have knocked me over with a feather," he said, "when I found out that people were talking about my wisdom and suggesting running me for President."

This, of course, offers a possibility for the future of the child itself. As soon as the boy makes up his mind just what type of man he wants to be, he could buy some crêpe hair and a bottle of spirit gum and make himself a pair of eyebrows to suit the rôle: converging toward the nose if he wants to be a judge or servant; pointing upward from the edge of the eyes if he wants to be a worried-looking man, like a broker; elevated to his forehead if he plans on simulating surprise as a personal characteristic; and in red patches if he intends being a stage Irishman.

In this way he may be able to get away with a great deal, as his pal the dog does.

pourquoi

ANONYMOUS

O Jean Baptiste, pourquoi,
O Jean Baptiste, pourquoi,
O Jean Baptiste,
Pourquoi you greased
My little dog's nose with tar?

Your little dog had catarrh,
Your little dog had catarrh,
And that was the reason
Why I have greasen
Your little dog's nose with tar.

O Jean Baptiste, I'm glad
O Jean Baptiste, I'm glad
O Jean Baptiste
I'm glad you greased
My little dog's nose with tar.

steig's dogs

"He's got it! The Frug!"

"Your spots are lovely."

"Get off my property!"

on cats and dogs

from *Idle Thoughts of an Idle Fellow*

JEROME K. JEROME

What I've suffered from them this morning no tongue can tell. It began with Gustavus Adolphus. Gustavus Adolphus (they call him "Gusty" downstairs for short) is a very good sort of dog, when he is in the middle of a large field, or on a fairly extensive common, but I won't have him indoors. He means well, but this house is not his size. He stretches himself, and over go two chairs and a what-not. He wags his tail, and the room looks as if a devastating army had marched through it. He breathes, and it puts the fire out.

At dinner-time he creeps in under the table, lies there for a while, and then gets up suddenly; the first intimation we have of his movements being given by the table, which appears animated by a desire to turn somersaults. We all clutch at it frantically, and endeavor to maintain it in a horizontal position; whereupon his struggles, he being under the impression that some wicked conspiracy is being hatched against him, become fearful, and the final picture presented is generally that of an overturned table and a smashed-up dinner, sandwiched between two sprawling layers of infuriated men and women.

He came in this morning in his usual style, which he appears to have founded on that of an American cyclone, and the first

24

thing he did was to sweep my coffee-cup off the table with his tail, sending the contents full into the middle of my waistcoat.

I rose from my chair, hurriedly, and remarking "————," approached him at a rapid rate. He preceded me in the direction of the door. At the door, he met Eliza, coming in with eggs. Eliza observed, "Ugh!" and sat down on the floor, the eggs took up different positions about the carpet, where they spread themselves out, and Gustavus Adolphus left the room. I called after him, strongly advising him to go straight downstairs, and not let me see him again for the next hour or so; and he, seeming to agree with me, dodged the coal-scoop, and went; while I returned, dried myself, and finished breakfast. I made sure that he had gone into the yard, but when I looked into the passage ten minutes later, he was sitting at the top of the stairs. I ordered him down at once, but he only barked and jumped about, so I went to see what was the matter.

It was Tittums. She was sitting on the top stair but one, and wouldn't let him pass.

Tittums is our kitten. She is about the size of a penny roll. Her back was up, and she was swearing like a medical student. . . . I told her she ought to be ashamed of herself, brought up in a Christian family as she was, too. I don't so much mind hearing an old cat swear, but I can't bear to see a mere kitten give way to it. It seems sad in one so young.

I put Tittums in my pocket, and returned to my desk. I forgot her for the moment, and when I looked I found that she had squirmed out of my pocket onto the table, and was trying to swallow the pen; then she put her leg into the ink-pot and upset it; then she licked her leg; then she swore again —at *me* this time.

I put her down on the floor, and there Tim began rowing with her. I do wish Tim would mind his own business. It was no concern of his what she had been doing. Besides, he is not a saint himself. He is only a two-year-old fox terrier, and he interferes with everything, and gives himself the airs of a gray-headed Scotch collie.

Tittums' mother has come in, and Tim has got his nose scratched, for which I am remarkably glad. I have put them all three out in the passage, where they are fighting at the present moment. I'm in a mess with the ink, and in a thundering bad temper; and if anything more in the cat or dog line comes fooling about me this morning, it had better bring its own funeral contractor with it. . . .

I wish people could love animals without getting maudlin over them, as so many do. Women are the most hardened offenders in such respects, but even our intellectual sex often degrade pets into nuisances by absurd idolatry. There are the gushing young ladies who, having read "David Copperfield," have thereupon sought out a small, long-haired dog of nondescript breed, possessed of an irritating habit of criticising a man's trousers, and of finally commenting upon the same by a sniff, indicative of contempt and disgust. They talk sweet girlish prattle to this animal (when there is anyone near enough to overhear them), and they kiss its nose, and put its unwashed head up against their cheek in a most touching manner; though I have noticed that these caresses are principally per-formed when there are young men hanging about.

Then there are the old ladies who worship a fat poodle, scant of breath, and full of fleas. I knew a couple of elderly spinsters once who had a sort of German sausage on legs, which they called a dog, between them. They used to wash its face with warm water every morning. It had a mutton cutlet regularly for breakfast; and on Sundays, when one of the ladies went to church, the other always stopped at home to keep the dog company.

There are many families where the whole interest of life is centred upon the dog. Cats, by the way, rarely suffer from

excess of adulation. A cat possesses a very fair sense of the ridic-
ulous, and will put her paw down kindly, but firmly, upon any
nonsense of this kind. Dogs, however, seem to like it. They
encourage their owners in the tomfoolery, and the consequence
is, that in the circles I am speaking of, what "dear Fido" has
done, does do, won't do, will do, can do, can't do, was doing,
is doing, is going to do, shan't do, and is about to be going to
have done, is the continual theme of discussion from morning
till night.

All the conversation, consisting, as it does, of the very dregs
of imbecility, is addressed to this confounded animal. The family sit in a row all day long, watching him, commenting upon
his actions, telling each other anecdotes about him, recalling
his virtues, and remembering with tears how one day they lost
him for two whole hours, on which occasion he was brought
home in a most brutal manner by the butcher boy, who had
been met carrying him by the scruff of his neck with one hand,
while soundly cuffing his head with the other.

After recovering from these bitter recollections, they vie with
each other in bursts of admiration for the brute, until some
more than usually enthusiastic member, unable any longer to
control his feelings, swoops down upon the unhappy quadru-
ped in a frenzy of affection, clutches it to his heart, and slob-
bers over it. Whereupon, the others, mad with envy, rise up,
and, seizing as much of the dog as greed of the first one has
left to them, murmur praise and devotion.

Among these people, everything is done through the dog. If
you want to make love to the eldest daughter, or get the old
man to lend you the garden roller, or the mother to subscribe
to the Society for the Suppression of Solo-cornet Players in
Theatrical Orchestras (it's a pity there isn't one, anyhow), you
have to begin with the dog. You must gain its approbation
before they will even listen to you, and if, as is highly probable, the animal, whose frank, doggy nature has been warped

by the unnatural treatment he has received, responds to your overtures of friendship by viciously snapping at you, your cause is lost forever.

If Fido won't take to anyone," the father has thoughtfully remarked beforehand, "I say that man is not to be trusted. You know, Maria, how often I have said that. Ah! *he* knows, bless him."

Drat him!

And to think that the surly brute was once an innocent puppy, all legs and head, full of fun and play, and burning with ambition to become a big, good dog, and bark like mother.

canine cuisine

from *The Parables of Peter Partout*

JOHN GOULD

The following letter was recently received, and we sent it over to Peppermint Corner with the thought that Mr. Peter Partout was the best person we knew of to give it a sensible reply:

To the Editor:

You won't believe this, but Jack Harmon and I want to know what you feed your dog. Not commercial foods, but something very special between you and your pet. We are compiling an animal cookbook, which we hope in its way will help feed many thousands of hungry animals.

Gratefully,
Astelle Atterbury

Southampton, New York

Mr. Partout's reply is about what we expected:

Dear Mrs. Atterbury:

My dog grew up in the pristine wilds of the Pine Tree State, and is accustomed to many fine dishes not always available in other places. Like roast beef. He found a fine roast of beef on the dining room table one day when he was just a puppy, and he liked it very much. I can report that he didn't like the cuffing he got afterwards, and as far as I know he has not made a habit of this delicacy. I presume you do not intend to run a recipe for roast beef for dogs in your cookbook, but if you do, be sure and include Yorkshire pudding —my dog loves it.

More to the point is Gelert, the dog I had before this one. He was hit by a school bus. But once he brought home a sixteen-prong deer's head. Gelert was part collie, part shepherd and part conjecture, and he was given to roaming the great wildwood in search of cates and dainties, and somehow he snagged onto this deer's head. I do not know if you folks in New York State know how this comes about. A gentleman in Maine who has by rare good chance accumulated a fine deer during that part of the year when the law is on usually keeps this a great secret. He doesn't blab. And after he has wrapped all the meat up in paper and marked it "lamb" and put it in the freezer, he will take the feet, skin and head and carry them to a far place and come away rapidly without them. Gelert just happened to find a head, and although it was twice the size of his own he muckled onto it and came hiking it home, his head held high so it wouldn't drag.

It so happened interestingly that Phil Mahany, who was game warden here for 20 years, was standing in my dooryard that morning discussing abstract philosophies with me on a friendly basis, and the time was last August. We hunt legally in November. So I'm standing there pondering the remarks of Warden Mahany, and I looks up and sees Gelert come around the corner of the barn with this deer's head. I trust the nuances of this tableau come through to you.

Gelert was a friendly dog, and he was proud of his prize. So he trots over and lays the deer's head at the feet of Warden Mahany and sits down wagging his tail to await the pat on his head which he expected. Warden Mahany continued the flow of discourse, and seemed not to notice this presen-

tation by Gelert. Gelert sat there a moment, and as the Warden neglected to speak to him or pat him he reached up with one paw and scraped it down the leg of Mahany's uniform to direct attention to the situation.

Mr. Mahany was a good warden, and subsequently he arrested a neighbor of mine down the road for poaching, and the neighbor admitted Gelert's 16-prong head was his, but I can tell you that for the nonce I was not having a good time. It is not the happiest juxtaposition of happenstance, in Maine, to be talking with a game warden and have your dog bring a deer's head from behind your barn. That is, for *you*. But for your dog, it is a rare and magnificent moment and you should put all this in your cookbook. While I was sweating lest Warden Mahany leap to an unwarranted conclusion, Gelert was jubilant.

After Gelert raked Mahany with his paw a few more times, the Warden reached down and patted him and said, "Nice doggie—bringing home the bacon, eh?" Now satisfied, Gelert next carried the deer's head up on the doorstep and began closer investigation of it with evident pleasure. Gelert was disposed to delicacies. He got the good of that deer's head several times over, and after he had lost interest in it I took it up in the pasture and buried it.

But I think you should get this into your book. Give a good dog recipe for deer's head. There is nothing a dog likes better. In addition to nourishing him, it contributes considerable healthful exercise, because he has to fight off all the other dogs who come around and try to steal it. He thus gets contact with other dogs his own age. You can feed a dog patent foods all his life, and they will never enrich his experiences the way a good deer's head will.

I would like to point out too that the owner of a dog with a deer's head finds his days enhanced. Apart from the visitations of a warden, the presence of a deer's head on your front steps makes for conversation. People notice it. Particularly in August. They comment on it, and sometimes go to the health officer. The owner of a dog with a deer's head will find little else in all his days that leads to so many pleasures. Your book, in short, should definitely have a chapter in it about deer's heads, and how to acquire them and prepare them for use. Nothing I have ever seen is as good. You will find it is something very special between you and your pet. I wish you success in your project.

(Signed)   PETER PARTOUT

PEPPERMINT CORNER

Illustrated by F. Wenderoth Saunders

fashions in dogs

E. B. WHITE

An Airedale, erect beside the chauffeur of a Rolls-Royce,
Often gives you the impression he's there from choice.

In town, the Great Dane
Is kept by the insane.

Today the boxer
Is fashionable and snappy;
But I never saw a boxer
Who looked thoroughly happy.

The Scotty's a stoic,
He's gay and he's mad;
His pace is a snail trot,
His harness is plaid.
I once had a bitch,
Semi-invalid, crazy:
There ne'er was a Scotch girl
Quite like Daisy.

Pekes
Are biological freaks.

They have no snout
And their eyes come out.
Ladies choose'm
To clutch to their bosom.
A Pekinese would gladly fight a wolf or a cougar
But is usually owned by a Mrs. Applegate Krueger.

Cockers are perfect for Elizabeth Barrett Browning,
Or to carry home a package from the A. & P. without clowning.

The wire-haired fox
Is hard on socks
With or without clocks.
The smooth-haired variety
Has practically vanished from nice society,
And it certainly does irk us
That you never see one except when you go to the circus.

The dachshund's affectionate,
He wants to wed with you:
Lie down to sleep,
And he's in bed with you.
Sit in a chair,
He's there.
Depart,
You break his heart.

My Christmas will be a whole lot wetter and merrier
If somebody sends me a six-weeks-old Boston terrier.

Sealyhams have square sterns and cute faces
Like toy dogs you see at Macy's.
But the Sealyham, while droll in appearance,
Has no clearance.

Chows come in black, and chows come in red;
They could come in bright green, I wouldn't turn my head.
The roof of their mouth is supposed to be blue,
Which is one of those things that might easily be true.

To us it has never seemed exactly pleasant
To see a beautiful setter on East Fifty-seventh Street looking
    for a woodcock or a pheasant.

German shepherds are useful for leading the blind,
And for biting burglars and Consolidated Edison men
    in the behind.

Lots of people have a rug.
Very few have a pug.

puppies for sale: cheap to good home

GRAHAM

GRAHAM

"Still no luck with the advertisement?"

SYVERSON

the dog that bit people

from *My Life and Hard Times*

JAMES THURBER

Probably no one man should have as many dogs in his life as
I have had, but there was more pleasure than distress in them
for me except in the case of an Airedale named Muggs. He
gave me more trouble than all the other fifty-four or -five
put together, although my moment of keenest embarrassment
was the time a Scotch terrier named Jeannie, who had just
had four puppies in the shoe closet of a fourth-floor apartment in New York, had the fifth and last at the corner of—
but we shall get around to that later on. Then, too, there was
the prize-winning French poodle, a great big black poodle—
none of your little, untroublesome white miniatures—who got
sick riding in the rumble seat of a car with me on her way to
the Greenwich Dog Show. She had a red rubber bib tucked
around her throat and, since a rainstorm came up when we
were halfway through the Bronx, I had to hold over her a
small green umbrella, really more of a parasol. The rain beat
down fearfully, and suddenly the driver of the car drove into
a big garage, filled with mechanics. It happened so quickly
that I forgot to put the umbrella down, and I shall always
remember the look of incredulity that came over the face of
the garageman who came over to see what we wanted. "Get
a load of this, Mac," he called to someone behind him.

But the Airedale, as I have said, was the worst of all my dogs. He really wasn't my dog, as a matter of fact; I came home from a vacation one summer to find that my brother Robert had bought him while I was away. A big, burly, choleric dog, he always acted as if he thought I wasn't one of the family. There was a slight advantage in being one of the family, for he didn't bite the family as often as he bit strangers. Still, in the years that we had him he bit everybody but Mother, and he made a pass at her once but missed. That was during the month when we suddenly had mice, and Muggs refused to do anything about them. Nobody ever had mice exactly like the mice we had that month. They acted like pet mice, almost like mice somebody had trained. They were so friendly that one night when Mother entertained at dinner the Friraliras, a club she and my father had belonged to for twenty years, she put down a lot of little dishes with food in them on the pantry floor so that the mice would be satisfied with that and wouldn't come into the dining room. Muggs stayed out in the pantry with the mice, lying on the floor, growling to himself—not at the mice, but about all the people in the next room that he would have liked to get at. Mother slipped out into the pantry once to see how everything was going. Everything was going fine. It made her so mad to see Muggs lying there, oblivious of the mice—they came running up to her—that she slapped him and he slashed at her, but didn't make it. He was sorry immediately, Mother said. He was always sorry, she said, after he bit someone, but we could not understand how she figured this out. He didn't act sorry.

Mother used to send a box of candy every Christmas to the people the Airedale bit. The list finally contained forty or more names. Nobody could understand why we didn't get rid of the dog. I didn't understand it very well myself, but we didn't get rid of him. I think that one or two people tried to poison Muggs—he acted poisoned once in a while—and old

Major Moberly fired at him once with his service revolver near the Seneca Hotel in East Broad Street—but Muggs lived to be almost eleven years old, and even when he could hardly get around, he bit a congressman who had called to see my father on business. My mother had never liked the congressman— she said the signs of his horoscope showed he couldn't be trusted (he was Saturn with the moon in Virgo)—but she sent him a box of candy that Christmas. He sent it right back, prob- ably because he suspected it was trick candy. Mother persu- aded herself it was all for the best that the dog had bitten him, even though father lost an important business asssocia- tion because of it. "I wouldn't be associated with such a man," Mother said. "Muggs could read him like a book."

We used to take turns feeding Muggs to be on his good side, but that didn't always work. He was never in a very good humor, even after a meal. Nobody knew exactly what was the

matter with him, but whatever it was it made him irascible, especially in the mornings. Robert never felt very well in the morning, either, especially before breakfast, and once when he came downstairs and found that Muggs had moodily chewed up the morning paper he hit him in the face with a grape- fruit and then jumped up on the dining room table, scatter-

ing dishes and silverware and spilling the coffee. Muggs' first
free leap carried him all the way across the table and into a
brass fire screen in front of the gas grate, but he was back
on his feet in a moment, and in the end he got Robert and
gave him a pretty vicious bite in the leg. Then he was all over
it; he never bit anyone more than once at a time. Mother
always mentioned that as an argument in his favor; she said he
had a quick temper but that he didn't hold a grudge. She was
forever defending him. I think she liked him because he
wasn't well. "He's not strong," she would say, pityingly, but
that was inaccurate; he may not have been well but he was
terribly strong.

One time my mother went to the Chittenden Hotel to call
on a woman mental healer who was lecturing in Columbus
on the subject of "Harmonious Vibrations." She wanted to
find out if it was possible to get harmonious vibrations into
a dog. "He's a large tan-colored Airedale," Mother explained.
The woman said she had never treated a dog, but she advised
my mother to hold the thought that he did not bite and would
not bite. Mother was holding the thought the very next morning when Muggs got the iceman, but she blamed that slip-up
on the iceman. "If you didn't think he would bite you, he
wouldn't," Mother told him. He stomped out of the house in
a terrible jangle of vibrations.

One morning when Muggs bit me slightly, more or less
in passing, I reached down and grabbed his short stumpy
tail and hoisted him into the air. It was a foolhardy thing to
do and the last time I saw my mother, about six months ago,
she said she didn't know what possessed me. I don't either,
except that I was pretty mad. As long as I held the dog off
the floor by his tail he couldn't get at me, but he twisted and
jerked so, snarling all the time, that I realized I couldn't hold
him that way very long. I carried him to the kitchen and flung
him onto the floor and shut the door on him just as he crashed

against it. But I forgot about the back stairs. Muggs went up
the back stairs and down the front stairs and had me cornered
in the living room. I managed to get up onto the mantelpiece
above the fireplace, but it gave way and came down with a
tremendous crash, throwing a large marble clock, several vases,
and myself heavily to the floor. Muggs was so alarmed by the
racket that when I picked myself up he had disappeared. We
couldn't find him anywhere, although we whistled and shouted,
until old Mrs. Detweiler called after dinner that night. Muggs
had bitten her once, in the leg, and she came into the living room only after we assured her that Muggs had run away.
She had just seated herself when, with a great growling and
scratching of claws, Muggs emerged from under a davenport
where he had been quietly hiding all the time, and bit her
again. Mother examined the bite and put arnica on it and told
Mrs. Detweiler that it was only a bruise. "He just bumped
you," she said. But Mrs. Detweiler left the house in a nasty
state of mind.

Lots of people reported our Airedale to the police, but my

father held a municipal office at the time and was on friendly terms with the police. Even so, the cops had been out a couple of times—once when Muggs bit Mrs. Rufus Sturtevant and again when he bit Lieutenant-Governor Malloy—but Mother told them that it hadn't been Muggs' fault but the fault of the people who were bitten. "When he starts for them, they scream," she explained, "and that excites him." The cops suggested that it might be a good idea to tie the dog up, but Mother said that it mortified him to be tied up and that he wouldn't eat when he was tied up.

Muggs at his meals was an unusual sight. Because of the fact that if you reached toward the floor he would bite you, we usually put his food plate on top of an old kitchen table with a bench alongside the table. Muggs would stand on the bench and eat. I remember that my mother's Uncle Horatio, who boasted that he was the third man up Missionary Ridge, was splutteringly indignant when he found out that we fed the dog on a table because we were afraid to put his plate on the floor. He said he wasn't afraid of any dog that ever lived and that he would put the dog's plate on the floor if we would give it to him. Robert said that if Uncle Horatio had fed Muggs on the ground just before the battle he would have been the first man up Missionary Ridge. Uncle Horatio was furious. "Bring him in! Bring him in now!" he shouted. "I'll feed the ——— on the floor!" Robert was all for giving him a chance, but my father wouldn't hear of it. He said that Muggs had already been fed. "I'll feed him again!" bawled Uncle Horatio. We had quite a time quieting him.

In his last year Muggs used to spend practically all of his time outdoors. He didn't like to stay in the house for some reason or other—perhaps it held too many unpleasant memories for him. Anyway, it was hard to get him to come in, and as a result the garbage man, the iceman, and the laundryman wouldn't come near the house. We had to haul the garbage down to the corner, take the laundry out and bring it back, and meet the iceman a block from home. After this had gone on for some time, we hit on an ingenious arrangement for getting the dog in the house so that we could lock him up while the gas meter was read, and so on. Muggs was afraid of only one thing, an electrical storm. Thunder and lightning frightened him out of his senses (I think he thought a storm had broken the day the mantelpiece fell). He would rush into the house and hide under a bed or in a clothes closet. So we fixed up a thunder machine out of a long narrow piece of sheet iron with a wooden handle on one end. Mother would shake this vigorously when she wanted to get Muggs into the house. It made an excellent imitation of thunder, but I suppose it was the most roundabout system for running a household that was ever devised. It took a lot out of Mother.

A few months before Muggs died, he got to "seeing things." He would rise slowly from the floor, growling low, and stalk stiff-legged and menacing toward nothing at all. Sometimes the Thing would be just a little to the right or left of a visitor. Once a Fuller Brush salesman got hysterics. Muggs came wandering into the room like Hamlet following his father's ghost. His eyes were fixed on a spot just to the left of the Fuller Brush man, who stood it until Muggs was about three slow, creeping paces from him. Then he shouted. Muggs wavered on past him into the hallway, grumbling to himself, but the Fuller Brush man went on shouting. I think Mother had to throw a pan of cold water on him before he stopped. That was the way she used to stop us boys when we got into fights.

Muggs died quite suddenly one night. Mother wanted to bury him in the family plot under a marble stone with some such inscription as "Flights of angels sing thee to thy rest" but we persuaded her it was against the law. In the end we just put up a smooth board above his grave along a lonely road. On the board I wrote with an indelible pencil *"Cave Canem."* Mother was quite pleased with the simple, classic dignity of the old Latin epitaph.

Illustrated by the author

the way old tige barked

AN AMERICAN FOLK TALE

There was once a backwoodsman who boasted that his hound Tige was the best hunting dog in seven counties. He said that he never went hunting that Tige did not tree a varmint and that by the way he barked old Tige always told him what the varmint was.

A newcomer to the settlement, who thought that the old-timer must be stretching the blanket a bit, offered to bet that old Tige could not tell one varmint from another. So to settle the wager the men went hunting the next night. They turned Tige loose in the creek bottom and told him to sic.

"There ain't no use in walking around a lot," said the backwoodsman. "Old Tige will let us know when he finds something."

They had not been sitting long when old Tige was heard.

"Jest wait," said the settler. "He ain't treed yet."

They sat for a few minutes longer, then old Tige sounded a new note.

"He's treed now," said the backwoodsman.

"What's he got?" asked the newcomer.

"I reckon that must be a bobcat."

When they reached the tree and held up their torch, sure enough there was a bobcat. They shot it and put Tige on the trial again.

After a while Tige bayed.

"He's treed," said the old-timer.

"What's he got this time?"

"I reckon that must be a possum."

They came to the tree, and sure enough there was the possum.

Again they sat while Tige ranged and again Tige bayed.

"What's Tige got this time?"

"I reckon that must be a coon."

Again the prediction proved correct.

The newcomer was ready to pay the wager, but the night was young and the old-timer was eager for more hunting. So Tige was put on the trail and presently he bayed again.

Then suddenly his bark changed to a long howl that seemed to shake the trees and hills.

"What's Tige got now?" asked the newcomer.

"Tige ain't got nothing," replied the backwoodsman, jumping to his feet. "Something's got Tige."

ascension and declination of sirius

COLIN HOWARD

There was enormous excitement when it became known that "they" were shooting a scene for a film outside a large house locally. After breakfast I decided I would stroll along for a look with Marcus, my St. Bernard dog.

I have complained about Marcus before. He is huge, handsome, and affable. He is also incredibly stupid and supernaturally lazy. I allowed him his usual half-hour siesta after breakfast to recover from the strain of getting up, and then summoned him for his walk. He lurched to his feet with a sigh of self-pity, and stumbled somnambulistically after me.

As a rule, we go only as far as the first corner, by which time we are both tired out—Marcus with the exertion, myself with the effort of keeping him going. When, after some argument, I made it clear to him we were going even farther afield this morning his reproachful eyes filled with tears.

The scene was one of frantic activity. A throbbing mobile generator roared deafeningly in a corner of the big garden. Herds of technicians were shoving around a camera built like a self-propelled gun, unreeling tape-measures, training things like searchlights, fooling about with yellow reflector-screens, swilling mugs of tea, and bustling about apparently just for the sake of looking busy. The spectacle of so much energy had a depressing effect on Marcus, and, realizing he was about to pass out on his flipper-like feet, I turned to take him home.

We hadn't got far when I heard somebody shouting and walking to catch us up. You don't have to run to catch up a man with a St. Bernard. I straightened my tie. Just at first, I confess, I thought—but it wasn't me; it was Marcus.

"Say!" said a young man with tousled hair and horn-rimmed glasses. "That's quite a dog!"

Marcus is responsive to admiration. He simpered, and even pranced a bit in a galumphing sort of way.

"We could use him," said the young man. "Would you hire him for the day for a couple of guineas?"

I said I would, and was instructed to bring Marcus back in a couple of hours. Two hours to get Marcus home, rest him up, and bring him back, was cutting it fine. We were nearly a quarter-mile from home. However, we set off. My wife was wildly excited by our news. She and I both went to work to groom Marcus for stardom.

It is not easy to groom a dog who is lying under the kitchen table in a state of physical prostration, but, with my wife on her knees on one side, myself on the other, and our heads meeting under the table, we managed to get him done, all except the bits of himself he was lying on.

Then came the terrific task of getting him back on location. We accomplished this by a little mild deceit. We pretended he had slept the clock round twice and it was now to-morrow. My wife came with us, partly because she wasn't going to miss Marcus's triumph, partly to push behind.

"We're shooting a crowd-scene—a garden-party," explained the director. He paused and tugged at his foot, on which Marcus had subsided in slumber. My wife and I deferentially prised up the appropriate portion of Marcus's body, and the director, having withdrawn his foot and found to his surprise no bones were broken, continued: "I want him to mingle with the crowd. I suggest your wife wave to him from the other side, and you release him when I nod and let him walk across the set."

At the word "walk" Marcus shuddered in his sleep.

My wife and I worked on Marcus like a couple of seconds on a boxer who has been saved by the bell. We got him to his feet, and I managed to hold him up while my wife took up her position. When the director nodded she waved and I let go of Marcus.

He fell down, bumping his nose, and went to sleep.

"What's the matter—is he ill?" demanded the director.

"No, no—it's just temperament," I laughed.

"Right, now! We're going to shoot this time!"

The hubbub was quadrupled. Men yelled "Okay!" at each other through a network of telephones. Buzzers sounded. Two lads without shoes shoved the camera slowly forward. The recording men dangled microphones on things like fishing-rods overhead. All the extras in their smart clothes minced and smiled. The clapper-boy stepped in front of the camera, exclaimed "Scene 92, Take 1," snapped his board, and stepped back.

"Shoot!" cried the director, and nodded at me.

Marcus took a game five steps forward towards my wife, faltered, and slumped to the ground. The cruising camera bumped into him and bounced back.

"Cut!" cried the director.

By late afternoon the clapper-boy was still the only one to have made anything like an extended appearance before the camera. After the first half-dozen takes we gave up trying to get Marcus away from scratch, and let him carry on from where he'd lain down last time. He was still only a third of the way across the set.

The clapper-boy took a voice-pastille, hoarsely recited "Scene 92, Take 21," and retired to get his chalk ready for Take 22. The director grimly muttered "Shoot!" I don't think he really expected anything to happen. But it did. My wife, seeing fame and fortune slipping from Marcus, had been inspired. She had found a cat and was holding it out enticingly.

Cats and food are the only things that ever induce Marcus to work like a real dog. I believe he confuses the two. He sighted the bait in my wife's arms. When the director said "Shoot!" he shot.

If Scene 92, Take 21, ever gets as far as the can the rushes will show a dazzling and aristocratic garden-party apparently smitten by a typhoon. One will see fair women and brave men, grave footmen and laden tea-trays, bowled over left and right by some mysterious agency moving too fast for the camera. My wife popped the cat into safety behind a wall with a split second to spare. Marcus hurtled into the wall, which rocked a bit but stood up well. My wife and I, just for a change, went around picking up extras.

And then the sun went in and rain-spots began to fall.

"Thank heaven!" said the director devoutly. "That's all for today. Same time tomorrow, please."

"Ask him if he wants Marcus again tomorrow," whispered my wife.

I glanced at the director, and decided not to. I took my wife's hand, and we started to sneak away.

"Please don't forget your dog," said the director.

Marcus of course was in his usual position—flat on the ground, resting. The extras bore no malice. They realized they had Marcus to thank for another day's work. They helped us to lift him more or less tenderly into the bus waiting to take them to the station and he was driven home in style, occupying three seats and a couple of laps, and absolutely insensible. They thought he had been stunned by the wall. They did not understand St. Bernards.

Marcus is now slowly recovering from his tremendous day, on the front doormat where the extras dumped him. His film career, I cannot help feeling, is at an end.

traveling with the neurotic dog

from *How to Live With a Neurotic Dog*

STEPHEN BAKER

For reasons that are probably clear to them alone, most dogs consider the insides of automobiles their private domain and will take stern measures to protect this area against intruders. Filling station attendants come under the heading of intruders. This presents something of a problem when the driver finds himself in need of gas.

To forestall close bodily contact between dog and gas station attendant, some drivers keep their windows closed throughout the transaction. Communication may be a little tricky under these circumstances, but not impossible.

Illustrated by Eric Gurney

Yell instructions from inside the car.

Use hand signals to indicate number of gallons wanted.

Roll windows down slightly to provide some contact with the man on the other side.

If nothing else works, take a calculated risk. Open the window completely.

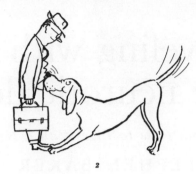

1

2

3

4

5

6

7

8

GIOVANNETTI

mr. fogerty

from *Biltmore Oswald*

THORNE SMITH

June 29th. I met a very pleasant dog yesterday, whom I called Mr. Fogerty because of his sober countenance and the benign but rather puzzled expression in his large, limpid eyes, which were almost completely hidden by his bangs. He was evidently a visitor in camp, so I took him around and introduced him to the rest of the dogs and several of the better sort of goats. In all of these he displayed a friendly but dignified interest seeming to question them on the life of the camp, how they liked the Navy and what they thought were the prospects for an early peace. He refused to be separated from me, however, and even broke into the mess hall, from which he was unceremoniously ejected, but not before he had gotten half of my ration. In some strange manner he must have found out from one of the other dogs my name and address and exactly where I swung, for in the middle of the night I awoke to hear a lonesome whining in the darkness beneath my hammock and then the sniff, sniff of an investigating nose. As I know how it feels to be lonely in a big black barracks in the dead of night I carefully descended to the deck and collected this animal—it was my old friend, Mr. Fogerty, and he was quite overjoyed at having once more found me. After licking my face in gratitude he sat back on his haunches and waited for me to do something amusing. I didn't have the heart to leave him there in the darkness. Dogs have a certain way about them that gets me every time. I lifted Mr. Fogerty, a huge hulk of a dog, with much care and adjusting of overlapping paws into my hammock, and received a kiss in the eye for my trouble. Then I followed Mr. Fogerty into the hammock and resumed my slumber, but not with much comfort. Mr. Fogerty is a large,

sprawly dog, who evidently has been used to sleeping in vast spaces and who sees no reason for changing a lifelong habit. Consequently he considered me in the nature of a piece of gratifying upholstery. He slept with his hind legs on my stomach and his front paws propped against my chin. When he scratched, as he not infrequently did, what I decided must be a flea, his hind leg beat upon the canvas and produced a noise not unlike a drum. Thus we slept, but through some miscalculation I must have slept over, for it seems that the Master-at-arms, a very large and capable Irishman, came and shook my hammock.

"Hit the deck there, sailor," he said, "shake a leg, shake a leg."

At this point Mr. Fogerty took it upon himself to peer over the side of the hammock to see who this disturber of peace and quiet could be. This was just a little out of the line of duty for the Jimmy-legs, and I can't say as I blame him for his conduct under rather trying circumstances. Mr. Fogerty has a large, shaggy head, not unlike a lion's, and his mouth, too, is quite large and contains some very long and sharp teeth. It seems that Mr. Fogerty, still heavy with slumber, quite naturally yawned into the horrified face of the Jimmy-legs, who, mistaking the operation for a hostile demonstration, retreated from the barracks with admirable rapidity for one so large, crying in a distracted voice as he did so:

"By the saints, it's a beast he's turned into during the night. Sure, it's a visitation of Providence, heaven preserve us."

It seems I have been washing hammocks ever since. Mr. Fogerty sits around and wonders what it's all about. I like Fogerty, but he gets me in trouble, and in this I need no help whatsoever.

Illustrated by Dick Dorgan

dogs that have known me

from *Please Don't Eat the Daisies*

JEAN KERR

I never meant to say anything about this, but the fact is that I have never met a dog that didn't have it in for me. You take Kelly, for instance. He's a wire-haired fox terrier and he's had us for three years now. I wouldn't say that he was terribly handsome but he does have a very nice smile. What he *doesn't* have is any sense of fitness. All the other dogs in the neighborhood spend their afternoons yapping at each other's heels or chasing cats. Kelly spends his whole day, every day, chasing swans on the millpond. I don't actually worry because he will never catch one. For one thing, he can't swim. Instead of settling for a simple dog paddle like everybody else, he has to show off and try some complicated overhand stroke, with the result that he always sinks and has to be fished out. Naturally, people talk, and I never take him for a walk that somebody doesn't point him out and say, "There's that crazy dog that chases swans."

Another thing about that dog is that he absolutely refuses to put himself in the other fellow's position. We have a pencil sharpener in the kitchen and Kelly used to enjoy having an occasional munch on the plastic cover. As long as it was just a nip now and then, I didn't mind. But one day he simply lost his head and ate the whole thing. Then I had to buy a new one and of course I put it up high out of Kelly's reach. Well, the scenes we were treated to—and the sulking! In fact, ever since he has been eating things I know he doesn't like just to get even. I don't mean things like socks and mittens and paper napkins, which of course are delicious. Lately he's been eating plastic airplanes, suede brushes, and light bulbs. Well, if he wants to sit under the piano and make low and loving growls over a suede brush just to show me, okay. But frankly I think he's lowering himself.

Time and again I have pointed out to Kelly that with discriminating dogs, dogs who are looking for a finer, lighter chew—it's bedroom slippers two to one. I have even dropped old, dilapidated bedroom slippers here and there behind the furniture, hoping to tempt him. But the fact is, that dog wouldn't touch a bedroom slipper if he was starving.

Although we knew that, as a gourmet, he was a washout, we did keep saying one thing about Kelly. We kept saying, "He's a good little old watchdog." Heaven knows why we thought so, except that he barks at the drop of a soufflé. In fact, when he's in the basement a stiff toothbrush on the third floor is enough to set him off into a concerto of deep, murderous growls followed by loud hysterical yappings. I used to take real pleasure in imagining the chagrin of some poor intruder who'd bring that cacophony upon himself. Last month we had an intruder. He got in the porch window and took twenty-two dollars and my wristwatch while Kelly, that good little old watchdog, was as silent as a cathedral. But that's the way it's been.

The first dog I remember well was a large black and white mutt that was part German shepherd, part English sheep dog, and part collie—the wrong part in each case. With what strikes me now as unforgivable whimsey, we called him Ladadog from the title by Albert Payson Terhune. He was a splendid dog in many respects but, in the last analysis, I'm afraid he was

a bit of a social climber. He used to pretend that he was just crazy about us. I mean, if you just left the room to comb your hair he would greet you on your return with passionate lickings, pawings, and convulsive tail-waggings. And a longer separation—let's say you had to go out on the front porch to pick up the mail—would set Ladadog off into such a demonstration of rapture and thanksgiving that we used to worry for his heart.

However, all this mawkish, slobbering sentiment disappeared the moment he stepped over the threshold. I remember we kids used to spot him on our way home from school, chasing around the Parkers' lawn with a cocker friend of his, and we'd rush over to him with happy squeals of "Laddy, oleboy, oleboy, oleboy," and Ladadog would just stand there looking slightly pained and distinctly cool. It wasn't that he cut us dead. He nodded, but it was with the remote air of a celebrity at a cocktail party saying, "Of *course* I remember you, and how's Ed?"

We kept making excuses for him and even worked out an elaborate explanation for his behavior. We decided that Ladadog didn't see very well, that he could only recognize us by smell and that he couldn't smell very well in the open air. However, the day came when my mother met Ladadog in front of the A & P. She was wearing her new brown coat with the beaver collar, and, lo and behold, Ladadog greeted her with joy and rapture. After that we just had to face the truth—that dog was a snob.

He also had other peculiarities. For instance, he saved lettuce. He used to beg for lettuce and then he would store it away in the cellar behind the coalbin. I don't know whether he was saving up to make a salad or what, but every so often we'd have to clean away a small, soggy lump of decayed vegetation.

And every time the phone rang he would run from wherever he was and sit there beside the phone chair, his tail thumping and his ears bristling, until you'd make some sort of an announcement like "It's just the Hoover man" or "Eileen, it's for you." Then he would immediately disappear. Clearly, this dog had put a call in to someone, but we never did figure out who.

Come to think of it, the dog that gave us the most trouble was a beagle named Murphy. As far as I'm concerned, the first thing he did wrong was to turn into a beagle. I had seen him bouncing around in the excelsior of a pet-shop window, and I went in and asked the man, "How much is that adorable fox terrier in the window?" Did he say, "That adorable fox terrier is a beagle?" No, he said, "Ten dollars, lady." Now, I don't mean to say one word against beagles. They have rights just like other people. But it is a bit of a shock when you bring home a small ball of fluff in a shoe box, and three weeks later it's as long as the sofa.

He had a habit that used to leave us open to a certain amount of criticism from our friends, who were not dogophiles. He never climbed up on beds or chairs or sofas. But he always sat on top of the piano. In the beginning we used to try to pull him off of there. But after a few noisy scuffles in which he knocked a picture off the wall, scratched the piano, and smashed a lamp, we just gave in—only to discover that, left to his own devices, he hopped up and down as delicately as a ballet dancer. We became quite accustomed to it, but at parties at our house it was not unusual to hear a guest remark, "I don't know what I'm drinking but I think I see a big dog on the piano."

It's not just our own dogs that bother me. The dogs I meet at parties are even worse. I don't know what I've got that attracts them; it just doesn't bear thought. My husband swears I rub chopped meat on my ankles. But at every party it's the same thing. I am sitting in happy conviviality with a group in front of the fire when all of a sudden the large mutt of mine host appears in the archway. Then, without a single bark of warning, he hurls himself upon me. It always makes me

think of that line from *A Streetcar Named Desire*—"Baby, we've had this date right from the beginning." My martini flies into space and my stockings are torn before he finally settles down peacefully in the lap of my new black faille. I blow out such quantities of hair as I haven't swallowed and glance at my host, expecting to be rescued. He murmurs, "Isn't that wonderful? You know, Brucie is usually so distant with strangers."

At a dinner party in Long Island last week, after I had been mugged by a large sheep dog, I announced quite piteously, "Oh dear, he seems to have swallowed one of my earrings." The hostess looked really distressed for a moment, until she examined the remaining earring. Then she said, "Oh, I think it will be all right. It's small and it's round."

Nowadays if I go anywhere I just ask if they have a dog. If they do, I say, "Maybe I'd better keep away from him—I have this bad allergy." This does not tend to endear me to my hostess. In fact, she behaves rather as though she'd just discovered that I was listed in "Red Channels." But it is safer. It really is.

Illustrated by Carl Rose

gallagher's dogs

"Why don't you hang out the window like other dogs?"

"Down, Fang!"

"Oh, they don't get any bigger than about so."

"I get you all the way to the vet and then you stop scratching!"

"Now, here comes the final test."

a dog's best friend
is his illiteracy

OGDEN NASH

It has been well said that quietness is what a Grecian urn
is the still unravished bride of,
And that a door is what a dog is perpetually on the wrong
side of.
I may add that a sachet is what many a housewife's linen is
fragrantly entrusted to,
But that a cliché is what a dog owner must eventually get
adjusted to.
Whether your visitor be Mr. Belvedere or Bennett Cerf, what
does he say when your dog greets him with Southern
hospitality and salutes him all kissin'-cousiny?
He says, He smells my dog on me, doesn't he?
And he asks, How old is he, and you say Twelve, and he
appraises Spot with the eye of an antiquarian,
And says, Seven twelves are eighty something, why Spot in
human terms you're an octogenarian,
But these two bromides are just the rattle before the strike,
Because then he says it's funny but he's noticed how often
dogs and their masters look alike.

66

Such are the comments faced by dog owners from Peoria to
    Peshawar,
And frequently from a man who in canine terms is 322 years
    old, and he is the spit and image of his Chihuahua.
The only escape is to have something instead of dogs but
    whatever I substituted I should probably err,
And if I ended up with raccoons every guest would turn out
    to be a raccoonteur.

making money out of dogs

a tale of the great depression

from *Modern Australian Humour*

LEN LOWER

"I've been readin' the paper, Bill, and I've got an idea."

"You don't say! Well, them newspapers must be improvin' outer sight. 'Ang out the flag—little Jimmy's got an idear."

"Listen to me. Work is as scarce in Sydney as the butter in a hot-dog."

"Too right, James. Too blooming true."

"Don't interrupt me, you igerant cow, or I'll take my singlet off you! As I was sayin' about this idea—you know the 'Lost and Found' column?"

"Yeah."

"Well, look at the hundreds of things that are lost every day and found by people who ain't lookin' for 'em. And the rewards! There's money just for the picking up!"

"Yes! I know—'Lost, small leather bag, containing slate and pencil, between Manly and Petersham. Finder keep slate, return bag'—and rolls of notes. Now, I ask you, Jimmie, did you ever 'ear of anyone finding a roll of notes? No! of course you didn't. It's a damn lie!"

"There's jewellery," suggested Jimmy.

"Huh! 'Angin' round waitin' for someone to drop their diamond tiara outer the tram."

68

"Well, what about lost cats and dogs?"

"Look 'ere! If you think I'm going to spend me time craw-lin' over roofs collecting cats, in the 'opes that one of 'em's lost—you're mistaken. My ruddy oath, you are!"

"Dogs," remarked Jimmy. "Now here's one: 'Lost, white pomeranium, black ears, answers to name of "Oozles".' You'd sight that dog out of a million. A white pom with black ears!"

Bill walked to the window and draped himself over the sill.

"A fine chance," he remarked to the street, "a man's got 'Oozlin' every dog 'e sees with—Hoi! Blime!"

With a rush that knocked his friend off the chair, Bill had left the window, and was now clattering down the stairs to the front door.

Jimmy picked himself up, and gazed out the window.

"Struth!" he yelled, and dived for the door.

Outside, a white pomeranian with black ears sniffed dis-gustedly at a banana skin in the gutter.

" 'Ead 'im orf!" gasped Bill.

Jimmy spat disgustedly over his shoulder:
"Nobody mistook me for Nurmi before," he panted. " 'Ead'im orf yourself."

The dog, not having the incentive of an urgent need of cash, gave in; and Bill, first on the scene, gathered him up.

"That your dog?"

"Eh?" said Bill, turning to the constable who had appar-ently manifested himself from a hole in the road.

"Course he's my dorg! I wouldn't be bustin' meself chasin' someone else's dorg. S'matter of fact, me and my mate (point-ing to Jimmy who had just lumbered up) were trainin' 'im. I tell y'constable (he dropped his voice to a whisper), first time we gives 'im a run at the tin 'are—be on 'im."

He moved off.

"Walk quick, you mug," said Jimmy fearfully. "They don't race pomeraniums after hares! You nearly cruelled it."

It was a long walk back.

"Well," said Bill, in the safety of their lodgings, "there 'e is."

"Yes," said Jimmy, gazing down at the dog.

"Poor liddle Oozles. Here, Oozles, Oozles!"

"Oh, Blime! Oozles!" said Bill, "what a name to give the poor little cow. No wonder 'e's got black ears. 'Ere, Stinker!"

The dog wearily wagged his busy tail.

"There, y'are!" said Bill, triumphantly. "'E knows a proper dorg's name when 'e 'ears it."

Jimmy was studying the paper again.

"He belongs to 'Dilhurst,' Darlinghurst Road. We'll give him that frankfurt you was keeping for your tea, and then I'll take him along."

"Orright," said Bill, "I'll starve."

Man and dog were gone an hour, when Bill, from his eyrie in the window, sighted them coming back.

"Aw, strike me pink!" he muttered, withdrawing himself from the window, "I knew 'e'd muck it up."

He sat on the bed, turning over in his mind a few pithy remarks to be delivered to James.

The door opened.

" 'Ullo, brains! What the 'ell did you bring the dorg back for? No wonder you can't get a job. You got about as much gumption as a politician—"

"Shut up, Sunshine! Gaze on this, an' apologize."

Two pound notes were waving before his eyes. His mouth opened.

"Now shut up!" said Jimmy. "I'll do all the talkin', same as I do all the thinkin'."

He seated himself on the bed and commenced.

"I goes up to the house, a big flash joint it is, knocks at the door, and a tony old tart comes as soon as she hears I've got the dog. 'My little Oozlums', she says. 'Diddums got losty wosty?' Fair make you vomit."

"She asks me a lot of questions, and I tells her 'ow I threw meself in front of a 'bus just in time to save him, and she comes to light with a quid."

"Well, I'm going out the gate, and there's a bloke waiting for me."

" 'Did you bring that damn dog back?' he says, real fierce."

" 'Yes,' I says, 'an' I had a hard job to fetch him.' "

" 'Lord!' he says, 'and I had a hell of a job losing him.' "

"He does his block."

" 'I don't want the rotten thing in the house,' he yaps. 'How much did my wife give you?' "

"I tells him a quid."

" 'Well, look here,' he says, 'here's another quid. You hang about, and I'll push him out the door when she's not looking, and you lose him! See! Lose him!' "

"Yes," said Bill. "Go on."

"Well, I waits, and sure enough out comes Oozles—"

"Stinker," amended Bill.

"And I pounces on him, and here we are."

With a flourish, Jimmy pocketed a pound and handed Bill the other.

"Well, what'll we do with the dorg?" said Bill.

"I got another idea," said James. "I'm goin' out now to buy him a chop and drink your health, William."

"I can't let you do everythink without 'elping you some-times," said Bill. "I'll go with you."

Next morning, an excited Bill was reading to his mate: "Lorst, a valuable white pomer-what's-its-name, with black ears. Strayed from 'Dilhurst,' Darlinghurst Road. Answers to name of Oozles. Reward £3. Detainer persecuted."

Jimmy smiled indulgently at his friend. "That was my other idea," he said calmly. "That's why I brought him back. It's your turn to find him now."

Bill gazed at him.

"Well, I won't say you're brainy; but for low cunning you'd beat a sackful of monkeys, Jimmy. I'm erstounded at you. I'll take Stinker up this afternoon."

"And after that we'll have to find another dog," said Jimmy. "This one'll be played out."

"You know, James, we could make a business of this dorg-findin'. 'Lorst dorgs recovered—findings executed with utmost dispatch'—an' all that. Work it up into a big business, an' sell out."

"I'll think it over," said Jimmy loftily.

Late that afternoon, Bill stood at the door of "Dilhurst."

"Yairs," Bill was saying, "the young 'ooligans had 'im tied on the tram line, an' I was just in time to stop the tram."

"Did you give them in charge?" asked the lady indignantly.

"Every bloomin' one of 'em, missus. Eleven there was—an' I 'ope for Stink—for Oozles' sake, they get six months each."

"Henry," she said, turning to a man who had appeared in the hallway, "this man has just brought my little Oozles back."

"Oh! Has he?"

He came to the door.

"Just wait a moment and I'll bring you your reward," said the lady to Bill, and disappeared.

"Where did you find that rotten pampered mongrel?" whispered the man. "You ought to have more sense than to bring the thing back here."

"But you lorst it!" said Bill, agape.

"Take it away! You curse—yes, and I am very pleased indeed to see that there are still men kind enough to take care of a defenceless doggie-woggie."

"Give this to the man and thank him nicely, Henry," said the lady from behind his back.

Three pounds changed hands, and disappeared into Bill's pocket.

"Well, I'll be goin'," said Bill.

"Stop!" hissed the man, gazing after his wife's retreating form.

"Here!"—A fiver!

"Here!"—the dog!

Bill took both.

"Take it to b————!"

"Bankstown?" suggested Bill.

"Bourke!" blurted the man. "Get!"

Bill got.

Contentedly Oozles trotted alongside him back to the lodging house.

Jim was there.

"Mug! Mug! Oh what a large, empty blooming mug! What did you bring him back for?"

"Gaze on this bunch," said Bill, flourishing the notes, "an' go down on yore bended knees an' weep tears of blood!"

"Willie," said James earnestly, "if that dog is seen with us, we'll get years in the cooler."

"Why?" said Bill, in amazement.

"You know that cop what saw us pick him up? Well, I seen him today and he buttons me. That old tart must have notified all the police stations about that dog. He's worth pounds and pounds! I didn't know how to get out of it, and I finishes up telling him the truth about us wanting to get the reward, and how we took him back, and it ain't our fault if he's lost again. We're alright now, because he was a decent John; but if we're seen with that dog again—we'll finish up eatin' with a wooden spoon!"

"Gaw!" exclaimed Bill.

"Did the bloke tell you to take him away?"

"Yeah. To Bankstown."

"That's the ticket! You take him to Bankstown, and leave him. Go now—better wrap him up in a parcel so no one'll see him."

The wrapping of a live dog in a newspaper is no easy job,

nor is it any easier keeping him in the parcel whilst going past policemen. Bill drew a huge sigh of relief as the train bore him back from Bankstown—dogless—and the two men spent a happy evening over several bottles and a bed-full of fish and chips.

It was therefore with feelings of intense horror that Bill viewed the spectacle of a dilapidated pomeranian dog wagging his tail on the mat next morning.

He called Jim, and pointed.

They looked at each other, and a telepathic vision of prison cells communicated itself to their minds.

"Wrap 'im again," said Bill tersely. "It's your turn to lose 'im this time."

In silence they wrapped him. Jim took him away, and some considerable time elapsed before he returned.

"Took him to Manly," he said, throwing his hat on the bed.

"Put yer 'at on again," said Bill.

"Why?"

"We're movin'."

"Why? What did she say?"

" 'Oo?"

"The landlady?"

"Nothink. She don't know we're goin'."

"Well, what—?"

"Do y'think," said Bill, getting annoyed, "we want to be 'ere when that damn dorg comes back?"

"Strike me! No. Got all my things?"

"I got your singlet an' the shavin' soap."

"That's right, come on. Walk soft."

confessions of a man who doesn't own a dog

BURGES JOHNSON

Josh Billings wrote: "There is no man so poor but what he can afford to keep one dog. And I have seen them so poor that they could afford to keep three."

I myself have owned as many as four, but I have owned them one at a time. True, there have been still other dogs that I did not really own which undoubtedly believed that they belonged to me; scrawny, motheaten pups, that established residence on my door mat and followed me at safe distances, wagging propitiating tails.

But it happens that now I do not own any dog. How long this condition may last I cannot say. But during its continuance I possess an oddly critical attitude of mind toward those that do.

I cannot understand, for instance, why my neighbors let their snappy pet live a day longer. Some time he will spoil a friendship, and what is a mere pup compared to a friendly bond between human beings?

I can vaguely remember that once when a dog of mine bit a small piece out of an acquaintance I felt myself deeply incensed against that man. I felt that if the facts were fully

known it would be discovered that he had goaded my dog wholly beyond the patient creature's endurance, or that he had unduly tempted it just before meal time. In any case it was not the dog's fault.

But now I see things more clearly; that shivering little canine spider next door snapped at me and I am confident it is the dog's judgment and not my personality that is at fault.

"You've no idea how bright Toto is!" says its owner with gushing enthusiasm. "Why, only the other day we shut her out by mistake, and, would you believe it, she stood up on her hind legs so that her front paws just reached the window sill and she put her little tweetums black nose against the pane and called to us! Now wasn't that bright? Yes, oo's as clever as real folks, isn't oo, Toto precious?"

Aside from the fact that Toto once snapped at me and that she looks like a large boiled rat with the St. Vitus dance I wish to testify under oath that I have seen her waltz into an overturned wastepaper basket and whine to be let out at the bottom because she didn't know enough to turn around and get out the way she went in.

Yes, there were times, I admit, and they may come again, when I buttonholed acquaintances and related instance after instance to prove my dog's intelligence. Yet I like to recall in my own defence that whenever I did own a dog it was a whole one. I was no homœopathist as a dog fancier.

I seem to have acquired in these days a distaste for certain demonstrations of canine affection.

"Why Rover jumped right up and kissed you!" And Rover's owner looks at me admiringly and a bit thoughtfully too, as though discovering in me for the first time qualities she had not hitherto suspected.

I should think he did kiss me. No one knows better than I what a thorough job it was. Heaven help me to feign pleasure or even indifference until I can get to soap and water.

I can remember that once I encouraged my dog to dig. It amused me to pretend I was burying a bone until I had persuaded him to take up the task. But now I see the matter differently.

"Just watch Scotty dig!—isn't he wonderful?"

"But," I protest feebly, "those are my radishes."

"Ah, but the poor dear has so few opportunities. Come here, Scotty. Come right here! He doesn't mind very well to-day, but usually it's just wonderful the way he minds!"

What is the matter with me? In these disillusioned days a dog is no more than a dog—except in certain cases when he is much less. Ah me, I perceive that I must acquire another Great Dane. He at least compels honesty.

If he digs a garden I cannot say, "Perhaps the cat did it."

A shell from a 13-meter gun might have done it, but not a cat. If he kisses me on the cheek I either like it or I don't. There can be no such thing as indifference. Yes, I am suffering from dogophobia. Only the possession of a whole dog will cure me.

Illustrated by John Held, Jr.

canines in the cellar

from *Thurber's Dogs*

JAMES THURBER

My brightest remembrance of the old house goes back to the confused and noisy second and last visit of Aunt Mary, who had cut her first visit short because she hated our two dogs —Judge, an irritable old pug, and Sampson, a restless water spaniel—and they hated her. She had snarled at them and they had growled at her all during her stay with us, and not even my mother remembers how she persuaded the old lady to come back for a weekend, but she did, and what is more, she cajoled Aunt Mary into feeding "those dreadful brutes" the evening she arrived.

In preparation for this seemingly simple act of household routine, my mother had spent the afternoon gathering up all the dogs of the neighborhood, in advance of Aunt Mary's appearance, and putting them in the cellar. I had been allowed to go with her on her wonderful forays, and I thought that we were going to keep all the sixteen dogs we rounded up. Such an adventure does not have to have logical point or purpose in the mind of a six-year-old, and I accepted as a remarkable but natural phenomenon my mother's sudden assumption of the stature of Santa Claus.

She did not always let my father in on her elaborate pranks, but he came home that evening to a house heavy with tension

and suspense, and she whispered to him the peculiar truth
that there were a dozen and a half dogs in the cellar, counting
our Judge and Sampson. "What are you up to now, Mame?"
he asked her, and she said she just wanted to see Aunt Mary's
face when the dogs swarmed up into the kitchen. She could
not recall where she had picked up all of the dogs, but I remem-
bered, and still do, that we had imprisoned the Johnson's Irish
terrier, the Eiseles' shepherd, and the Mitchells' fox terrier,
among others. "Well, let's get it over with, then," my father
said nervously. "I want to eat dinner in peace, if that is possible."

The big moment finally arrived. My mother, full of smiles
and insincerity, told Aunt Mary that it would relieve her of
a tedious chore—and heaven knows, she added, there were a
thousand steps to take in that big house—if the old lady would
be good enough to set down a plate of dog food in the kitchen
at the head of the cellar stairs and call Judge and Sampson to
their supper. Aunt Mary growled and grumbled, and consigned
all dogs to the fires of hell, but she grudgingly took the plate
and carried it to the kitchen, with the Thurber family on her
heels. "Heavenly days!" cried Aunt Mary. "Do you make a cere-
mony out of feeding these brutes?" She put the plate down
and reached for the handle of the door.

None of us has even been able to understand why bedlam
hadn't broken loose in the cellar long before this, but it hadn't.
The dogs were probably so frightened by their unique predicament that their belligerence had momentarily left them.
But when the door opened and they could see the light of freedom and smell the odor of food, they gave tongue like a pack
of hunting hounds. Aunt Mary got the door halfway open and
the bodies of three of the largest dogs pushed it the rest of
the way. There was a snarling, barking, yelping swirl of yellow and white, black and tan, gray and brindle as the dogs
tumbled into the kitchen, skidded on the linoleum, sent the
food flying from the plate, and backed Aunt Mary into a cor-

ner. "Great God Almighty!" she screamed. "It's a dog factory!" She was only five feet tall, but her counterattack was swift and terrible. Grabbing a broom, she opened the back door and the kitchen windows and began to beat and flail at the army of canines, engaged now in half a dozen separate battles over the scattered food. Dogs flew out the back door and leaped through the windows, but some of them ran upstairs, and three or four others hid under sofas and chairs in the parlor. The indignant snarling and cursing of Judge and Sampson rose above even the laughter of my mother and the delighted squeals of her children. Aunt Mary whammed her way from room to room, driving dogs ahead of her. When the last one had departed and the upset house had been put back in order, my father said to his wife, "Well, Mame, I hope you're satisfied." She was.

Aunt Mary, toward the end of her long life, got the curious notion that it was my father and his sons, and not my mother, who had been responsible for the noisy flux of "all those brutes." Years later, when we visited the old lady on one of her birthdays, she went over the story again, as she always did, touching it up with distortions and magnifications of her own. Then she looked at the male Thurbers in slow, rueful turn, sighed deeply, gazed sympathetically at my mother, and said, in her hollowest tone, "Poor Mary!"

My mother's life with animals had been an arduous one since, as a little girl, she had lost a cranky but beloved parrot which had passed some ugly remarks to a big barnyard rooster and got killed for its impudence. She never owned another bird of any kind after that, but as the mother of three sons, and an admirer of dogs in her own right, she was destined to a life partly made up of canine frolic and frenzy. She once told me about a paraphrase of Longfellow that had been spoken to her in a dream: "And the cares that infest the day shall fold their tents like the Airedales and as silently steal away." This

must have come to her, of course, during the troublesome period of the Thurbers' life with Muggs, the Airedale that bit
people. But Muggs came later, after Rex, and after quite a
series of impermanent strays that Mary Thurber's sons lugged
home or that naturally found their way to a house containing
three boys. One of these was a young German shepherd that
we had picked up at a football game and later restored to
its lost owners. Another was an amiable nondescript that turned
up one day from nowhere, spent the weekend, and silently
stole away after eating my youngest brother's starfish, a dead,
dried starfish which Robert kept on a table with a shark's
tooth and a trap-door spider's nest, which were left untouched.

My grandfather's collie used to spend as much time at our
house as at his own, until the advent of Rex. Both the collie
and Rex were demon retrievers, fond of chasing a baseball
thrown down the street. One day the collie got to the ball first,
only to have Rex snatch it from his mouth and bring it back
to us on the gallop. The two dogs delayed the fight over this
incident until that afternoon in the parlor. It was possibly
the longest and certainly the noisiest dogfight ever staged in an
American parlor, and there were blood and hair and broken
Victrola records and torn lace curtains and smashed ash trays
all over the place before we got the battlers separated. The
collie, as the aggrieved party, had made the opening slash, and
Rex liked nothing better than an opening slash. The long
battle ended in a draw and in the departure of the collie for
good. He never came back to visit us again.

a radical flea

DON MARQUIS

dear boss i wish you would speak
to that lazy good for nothing
boston bull terrier of yours
whom you call pete
pete has got the idea lately
that he is a great hunter
i saw him stage a dramatic battle
with a grass hopper yesterday
and he nearly won it too
and this morning he made an entirely
unprovoked attack on me
it was only by retreating into
the mechanism of your typewriter
that i saved my life
some day i will set mehitabel on him
she can lick any bull terrier who ever lived
she will make ribbons out of that pete
and they wont be dog show ribbons either
as for his pretensions to being a thoroughbred
i take no stock in them
i asked a flea of his about it
recently and the flea said

i doubt peters claim to aristocracy
very much he does not look like
an aristocrat to me
and more than that he does not taste like one
i have bit some pretty swell dogs
in my time and i ought to know
if pete is an aristocrat
then i am a bengal tiger
but in hard times like these
a flea has got to put up with
any kind of dog he can get hold of
back in 1928 when things were booming
i wouldnt look at anything
but a dachshund with a pedigree
as long as himself
if the government doesnt start
to putting out a better brand of dogs
at federal expense
a lot of us fleas are going
to turn communist in a big way
if there was any justice in this country
they would give us russian wolf hounds
i find a lot of discontent among
insects in these days

                                        archy the cockroach

when the dogs take over

"You're spoiling him something terrible!"

LORIOT

"Hands up!"

LORIOT

the go-getter

from *Blandings Castle*

P. G. WODEHOUSE

On the usually unruffled brow of the Hon. Freddie Threepwood as he paced the gardens of Blandings Castle, there was
the slight but well-marked frown of one whose mind is not at
rest. It was high summer and the gardens were at their love-
liest, but he appeared to find no solace in their splendour.
Calceolarias, which would have drawn senile yips of ecstasy
from his father, Lord Emsworth, left him cold. He eyed the
lobelias with an unseeing stare, as if he were cutting an unde-
sirable acquaintance in the paddock at Ascot.

What was troubling this young man was the continued sales-
resistance of his Aunt Georgiana. Ever since his marriage to
the only daughter of Donaldson's Dog-Biscuits, of Long Island
City, N.Y., Freddie Threepwood had thrown himself heart
and soul into the promotion of the firm's wares. And, sent home
to England to look about for likely prospects, he had seen in
Georgiana, Lady Alcester, as has been already related, a cus-
tomer who approximated to the ideal. The owner of four
Pekingese, two Poms, a Yorkshire terrier, five Sealyhams, a
Borzoi and an Airedale, she was a woman who stood for something in dog-loving circles. To secure her patronage would be
a big thing for him. It would stamp him as a live wire and a
go-getter. It would please his father-in-law hugely. And the

proprietor of Donaldson's Dog-Joy was a man who, when even
slightly pleased, had a habit of spraying five-thousand-dollar
cheques like a geyser.

And so far, despite all his eloquence, callously oblivious of
the ties of kinship and the sacred obligations they involve,
Lady Alcester had refused to sign on the dotted line, preferring
to poison her menagerie with some degraded garbage called,
if he recollected rightly, Peterson's Pup-Food.

A bitter snort escaped Freddie. It was still echoing through
the gardens when he found that he was no longer alone. He
had been joined by his cousin Gertrude.

"What ho!" said Freddie amiably. He was fond of Gertrude,
and did not hold it against her that she had a mother who
was incapable of spotting a good dog-biscuit when she saw one.
Between him and Gertrude there had long existed a firm alli-
ance. It was to him that Gertrude had turned for assistance
when the family were trying to stop her getting engaged to
good old Beefy Bingham: and he had supplied assistance in
such good measure that the engagement was now an accepted
fact and running along nicely.

"Freddie," said Gertrude, "may I borrow your car?"

"Certainly. Most decidedly. Going over to see old Beefers?"

"No," said Gertrude, and a closer observer than her cousin
might have noted in her manner a touch of awkwardness. "Mr.
Watkins wants me to drive him to Shrewsbury."

"Oh? Well, carry on, as far as I'm concerned. You haven't
seen your mother anywhere, have you?"

"I think she's sitting on the lawn."

"Ah? Is she? Right-ho. Thanks."

Freddie moved off in the direction indicated, and presently
came in sight of his relative, seated as described. The Airedale
was lying at her feet. One of the Pekes occupied her lap. And
she was gazing into the middle distance in a preoccupied manner, as if she, like her nephew, had a weight on her mind.

Nor would one who drew this inference from her demeanour have been mistaken. Lady Alcester was feeling disturbed.

A woman who stands *in loco parentis* to fourteen dogs must of necessity have her cares, but it was not the dumb friends that were worrying Lady Alcester now. What was troubling her was the disquieting behaviour of her daughter Gertrude.

Engaged to the Rev. Rupert Bingham, Gertrude seemed to her of late to have become infatuated with Orlo Watkins, the Crooning Tenor, one of those gifted young men whom Lady Constance Keeble, the chatelaine of Blandings, was so fond of inviting down for lengthy visits in the summer-time.

On the subject of the Rev. Rupert Bingham, Lady Alcester's views had recently undergone a complete change. In the beginning, the prospect of having him for a son-in-law had saddened and distressed her. Then, suddenly discovering that he was the nephew and heir of as opulent a shipping magnate as ever broke bread at the Adelphi Hotel, Liverpool, she had soared from the depths to the heights. She was now strongly pro-Bingham. She smiled upon him freely. Upon his appointment to the vacant Vicarage of Much Matchingham, the village nearest to Market Blandings, she had brought Gertrude to the Castle so that the young people should see one another frequently.

And, instead of seeing her betrothed frequently, Gertrude seemed to prefer to moon about with this Orlo Watkins, this Crooning Tenor. For days they had been inseparable.

Now, everybody knows what Crooning Tenors are. Dangerous devils. They sit at the piano and gaze into a girl's eyes and sing in a voice that sounds like gas escaping from a pipe about Love and the Moonlight and You: and, before you know where you are, the girl has scrapped the deserving young clergyman with prospects to whom she is affianced and is off and away with a man whose only means of livelihood consist of intermittent engagements with the British Broadcasting Corporation.

If a mother is not entitled to shudder at a prospect like that, it would be interesting to know what she is entitled to shudder at.

Lady Alcester, then, proceeded to shudder: and was still shuddering when the drowsy summer peace was broken by a hideous uproar. The Peke and the Airedale had given tongue simultaneously, and, glancing up, Lady Alcester perceived her nephew Frederick approaching.

And what made her shudder again was the fact that in Freddie's eye she noted with concern the familiar go-getter gleam, the old dog-biscuit glitter.

However, as it had sometimes been her experience, when cornered by her nephew, that she could stem the flood by talking promptly on other subjects, she made a gallant effort to do so now.

"Have you seen Gertrude, Freddie?" she asked.

"Yes. She borrowed my car to go to Shrewsbury."

"Alone?"

"No. Accompanied by Watkins. The Yowler."

A further spasm shook Lady Alcester.

"Freddie," she said, "I'm terribly worried."

"Worried?"

"About Gertrude."

Freddie dismissed Gertrude with a gesture.

"No need to worry about her," he said. "What you want to worry about is these dogs of yours. Notice how they barked at me? Nerves. They're a mass of nerves. And why? Improper feeding. As long as you mistakenly insist on giving them Peterson's Pup-Food—lacking, as it is, in many of the essential vitamins—so long will they continue to fly off the handle every time they see a human being on the horizon. Now, pursuant on what we were talking about this morning, Aunt Georgiana, there is a little demonstration I would like . . ."

"Can't you give her a hint, Freddie?"

"Who?"

"Gertrude."

"Yes, I suppose I could give her a hint. What about?"

"She is seeing far too much of this man Watkins."

"Well, so am I, for the matter of that. So is everybody who sees him more than once."

"She seems quite to have forgotten that she is engaged to Rupert Bingham."

"Rupert Bingham, did you say?" said Freddie with sudden animation. "I'll tell you something about Rupert Bingham. He has a dog named Bottles who has been fed from early youth on Donaldson's Dog-Joy, and I wish you could see him. Thanks to the bone-forming properties of Donaldson's Dog-Joy, he glows with health. A fine, upstanding dog, with eyes sparkling with the joy of living and both feet on the ground. A credit to his master."

"Never mind about Rupert's dog!"

"You've got to mind about Rupert's dog. You can't afford to ignore him. He is a dog to be reckoned with. A dog that counts. And all through Donaldson's Dog-Joy."

"I don't want to talk about Donaldson's Dog-Joy."

"I do. I want to give you a demonstration. You may not know it, Aunt Georgiana, but over in America the way we advertise this product, so rich in bone-forming vitamins, is as follows: We instruct our demonstrator to stand out in plain view before the many-headed and, when the audience is of sufficient size, to take a biscuit and break off a piece and chew it. By this means we prove that Donaldson's Dog-Joy is so superbly wholesome as actually to be fit for human consumption. Our demonstrator not only eats the biscuit—he enjoys it. He rolls it round his tongue. He chews it and mixes it with his saliva . . ."

"Freddie, please!"

"With his saliva," repeated Freddie firmly. "And so does

the dog. He masticates the biscuit. He enjoys it. He becomes a bigger and better dog. I will now eat a Donaldson's Dog-Biscuit."

And before his aunt's nauseated gaze he proceeded to attempt this gruesome feat.

It was an impressive demonstration, but it failed in one particular. To have rendered it perfect, he should not have choked. Want of experience caused the disaster. Long years of training go to the making of the seasoned demonstrators of Donaldson's Dog-Joy. They start in a small way with carpet-tack and work up through the flat-irons and patent breakfast cereals till they are ready for the big effort. Freddie was a novice. Endeavoring to roll the morsel round his tongue, he allowed it to escape into his windpipe.

The sensation of having swallowed a mixture of bricks and sawdust was succeeded by a long and painful coughing fit. And when at length the sufferer's eyes cleared, no human form met their gaze. There was the Castle. There was the lawn. There were the gardens. But Lady Alcester had disappeared.

However, it is a well-established fact that good men, like Donaldson's Dog-Biscuits, are hard to keep down. Some fifty minutes later, as the Rev. Rupert Bingham sat in his study at Matchingham Vicarage, the parlourmaid announced a visitor. The Hon. Freddie Threepwood limped in, looking shop-soiled.

"What ho, Beefers," he said. "I just came to ask if I could borrow Bottles."

He bent to where the animal lay on the hearth-rug and prodded it civilly in the lower ribs. Bottles waved a long tail in brief acknowledgment. He was a fine dog, though of uncertain breed. His mother had been a popular local belle with a good deal of sex-appeal, and the question of his paternity was one that would have set a Genealogical College pursing its lips perplexedly.

"Oh, hullo, Freddie," said the Rev. Rupert.

The young Pastor of Souls spoke in an absent voice. He was

frowning. It is a singular fact—and one that just goes to show what sort of a world this is—that of the four foreheads introduced so far to the reader of this chronicle, three have been corrugated with care. And, if girls had consciences, Gertrude's would have been corrugated, too—giving us a full hand.

"Take a chair," said the Rev. Rupert.

"I'll take a sofa," said Freddie, doing so. "Feeling a bit used up. I had to hoof it all the way over."

"What's happened to your car?"

"Gertrude took it to drive Watkins to Shrewsbury."

The Rev. Rupert sat for a while in thought. His face, which was large and red, had a drawn look. Even the massive body which had so nearly won him a Rowing Blue at Oxford gave the illusion of having shrunk. So marked was his distress that even Freddie noticed it.

"Something up, Beefers?" he inquired.

For answer the Rev. Rupert extended a ham-like hand which held a letter. It was written in a sprawling, girlish handwriting.

"Read that."

"From Gertrude?"

"Yes. It came this morning. Well?"

Freddie completed his perusal and handed the document back. He was concerned.

"I think it's the bird," he said.

"So do I."

"It's long," said Freddie, "and it's rambling. It is full of stuff about 'Are we sure?' and 'Do we know our own minds?' and 'Wouldn't it be better, perhaps?' But I think it is the bird."

"I can't understand it."

Freddie sat up.

"I can," he said. "Now I see what Aunt Georgiana was drooling about. Her fears were well founded. The snake Watkins has stolen Gertrude from you."

"You think Gertrude's in love with Watkins?"

"I do. And I'll tell you why. He's a yowler, and girls always fall for yowlers. They have a glamour."

"I've never noticed Watkins's glamour. He has always struck me as a bit of a weed."

"Weed he may be, Beefers, but, none the less, he knows how to do his stuff. I don't know why it should be, but there is a certain type of tenor voice which acts on girls like catnip on a cat."

The Rev. Rupert breathed heavily.

"I see," he said.

"The whole trouble is, Beefers," proceeded Freddie, "that Watkins is romantic and you're not. Your best friend couldn't call you romantic. Solid worth, yes. Romance, no."

"So it doesn't seem as if there was much to be done about it?"

Freddie reflected.

"Couldn't you manage to show yourself in a romantic light?"

"How?"

"Well—stop a runaway horse."

"Where's the horse?"

"M'yes," said Freddie. "That's by way of being the difficulty, isn't it? The horse—where is it?"

There was silence for some moments.

"Well, be that as it may," said Freddie. "Can I borrow Bottles?"

"What for?"

"Purposes of demonstration. I wish to exhibit him to my Aunt Georgiana, so that she may see for herself to what heights of robustness a dog can rise when fed sedulously on Donaldson's Dog-Joy. I'm having a lot of trouble with that woman, Beefers. I try all the artifices which win to success in salesmanship, and they don't. But I have a feeling that if she could see Bottles and poke him in the ribs and note the firm, muscular flesh, she might drop. At any rate, it's worth trying. I'll take him along, may I?"

"All right."

"Thanks. And, in regard to your little trouble, I'll be giving it my best attention. You're looking in after dinner tonight ?"

"I suppose so," said the Rev. Rupert moodily.

The information that her impressionable daughter had gone off to roam the countryside in a two-seater car with the perilous Watkins had come as a grievous blow to Lady Alcester. As she sat on the terrace, an hour after Freddie had begun the weary homeward trek from Matchingham Vicarage, her heart was sorely laden.

The Airedale had wandered away upon some private ends, but the Peke lay slumbering in her lap. She envied it its calm detachment. To her the future looked black and the air heavy with doom.

Only one thing mitigated her depression. Her nephew Frederick had disappeared. Other prominent local pests were present, such as flies and gnats, but not Frederick. The grounds of Blandings Castle appeared to be quite free from him.

And then even this poor consolation was taken from the stricken woman. Limping a little, as if his shoes hurt, the Hon. Freddie came round the corner of the shrubbery, headed in her direction. He was accompanied by something having the outward aspect of a dog.

"What ho, Aunt Georgiana!"

"Well, Freddie?" sighed Lady Alcester resignedly.

The Peke, opening one eye, surveyed the young man for a moment, seemed to be debating within itself the advisability of barking, came apparently to the conclusion that it was too hot, and went to sleep again.

"This is Bottles," said Freddie.

"Who?"

"Bottles. The animal I touched on some little time back. Note the well-muscled frame."

"I never saw such a mongrel in my life."

"Kind hearts are more than coronets," said Freddie. "The point at issue is not this dog's pedigree, which, I concede, is not all Burke and Debrett, but his physique. Reared exclusively on a diet of Donaldson's Dog-Joy, he goes his way with his chin up, frank and fearless. I should like you, if you don't mind, to come along to the stables and watch him among the rats. It will give you some idea."

He would have spoken further, but at this point something occurred, as had happened during his previous sales talk, to mar the effect of Freddie's oratory.

The dog Bottles, during this conversation, had been roaming to and fro in the inquisitive manner customary with dogs who find themselves in strange territory. He had sniffed at trees. He had rolled on the turf. Now, returning to the centre of things, he observed for the first time that on the lap of the woman seated in the chair there lay a peculiar something.

What it was Bottles did not know. It appeared to be alive. A keen desire came upon him to solve this mystery. To keep the records straight, he advanced to the chair, thrust an inquiring nose against the object, and inhaled sharply.

The next moment, to his surprise, the thing had gone off like a bomb, sprung to the ground, and was moving rapidly towards him.

Bottles did not hesitate. A rough-and-tumble with one of his peers he enjoyed. He, as it were, rolled it round his tongue and mixed it with his saliva. But this was different. He had never met a Pekingese before, and no one would have been more surprised than himself if he had been informed that this curious, fluffy thing was a dog. Himself, he regarded it as an Act of God, and, thoroughly unnerved, he raced three times round the lawn and tried to climb a tree. Failing in this endeavor, he fitted his ample tail if possible more firmly into its groove and vanished from the scene.

The astonishment of the Hon. Freddie Threepwood was only equalled by his chagrin. Lady Alcester had begun now to express her opinion of the incident, and her sneers, her jeers, her unveiled innuendoes were hard to bear. If, she said, the patrons of Donaldson's Dog-Joy allowed themselves to be chased off the map in this fashion by Pekingese, she was glad she had never been weak enough to be persuaded to try it.

"It's lucky," said Lady Alcester in her hard, scoffing way, "that Susan wasn't a rat. I suppose a rat would have given that mongrel of yours heart failure."

"Bottles," said Freddie stiffly, "is particularly sound on rats. I think, in common fairness, you ought to step to the stables and give him a chance of showing himself in a true light."

"I have seen quite enough, thank you."

"You won't come to the stables and watch him dealing with rats?"

"I will not."

"In that case," said Freddie sombrely, "there is nothing more to be said. I suppose I may as well take him back to the Vicarage."

"What Vicarage?"

"Matchingham Vicarage."

"Was that Rupert's dog?"

"Of course it was."

"Then have you seen Rupert?"

"Of course I have."

"Did you warn him? About Mr. Watkins?"

"It was too late to warn him. He had had a letter from Gertrude, giving him the raspberry."

"What!"

"Well, she said Was he sure and Did they know their own minds, but you can take it from me that it was tantamount to the raspberry. Returning, however, to the topic of Bottles, Aunt Georgiana, I think you ought to take into consideration

the fact that, in his recent encounter with the above Peke,
he was undergoing a totally new experience and naturally did
not appear at his best. I repeat once more that you should see
him among the rats."

"Oh, Freddie!"

"Hullo?"

"How can you babble about this wretched dog when
Gertrude's whole future is at stake? It is simply vital that somehow she be cured of this dreadful infatuation . . ."

"Well, I'll have a word with her if you like, but, if you ask
me, I think the evil has spread too far. Watkins has yowled
himself into her very soul. However, I'll do my best. Excuse
me, Aunt Georgiana."

From a neighbouring bush the honest face of Bottles was
protruding. He seemed to be seeking assurance that the All
Clear had been blown.

It was at the hour of the ante-dinner cocktail that Freddie
found his first opportunity of having the promised word with
Gertrude. Your true salesman and go-getter is never beaten,
and a sudden and brilliant idea for accomplishing the conver-
sion of his Aunt Georgiana had come to him as he brushed
his hair. He descended to the drawing-room with a certain
jauntiness, and was reminded by the sight of Gertrude of his
mission. The girl was seated at the piano, playing dreamy chords.

"I say," said Freddie, "a word with you, young Gertrude.
What is all this bilge I hear about you and Beefers?"

The girl flushed.

"Have you seen Rupert?"

"I was closeted with him this afternoon. He told me all."

"Oh?"

"He's feeling pretty low."

"Oh?"

"Yes," said Freddie, "pretty low the poor old chap is feeling,
and I don't blame him, with the girl he's engaged to rushing

about the place getting infatuated with tenors. I never heard of such a thing, dash it! What do you see in this Watkins? Wherein lies his attraction? Certainly not in his ties. They're awful. And the same applies to his entire outfit. He looks as if he had bought his clothes off the peg at a second-hand gents' costumiers. And, as if that were not enough, he wears short, but distinct, side-whiskers. You aren't going to tell me that you're seriously considering chucking a sterling egg like old Beefers in favour of a whiskered warbler?''

There was a pause. Gertrude played more dreamy chords.

"I'm not going to discuss it," she said. "It's nothing to do with you."

"Pardon me!" said Freddie. "Excuse me! If you will throw your mind back to the time when Beefers was conducting his wooing, you may remember that I was the fellow who worked the whole thing. But for my resource and ingenuity you and the old bounder would never have got engaged. I regard myself, therefore, in the light of a guardian angel or something; and as such am entitled to probe the matter to its depths. Of course," said Freddie, "I know exactly how you're feeling. I see where you have made your fatal bloomer. This Watkins has cast his glamorous spell about you, and you're looking on Beefers as a piece of unromantic cheese. But mark this, girl . . ."

"I wish you wouldn't call me 'girl.' "

"Mark this, old prune," amended Freddie. "And mark it well. Beefers is tried, true and trusted. A man to be relied on. Whereas Watkins, if I have read those whiskers aright, is the sort of fellow who will jolly well let you down in a crisis. And then, when it's too late, you'll come moaning to me, weeping salt tears and saying, 'Ah, why did I not know in time?' And I shall reply, 'You unhappy little fathead . . . !' "

"Oh, go and sell your dog-biscuits, Freddie!"

Gertrude resumed her playing. Her mouth was set in an obstinate line. Freddie eyed her with disapproval.

"It's some taint in the blood," he said. "Inherited from female parent. Like your bally mother, you are constitutionally incapable of seeing reason. Pig-headed, both of you. Sell my dog-biscuits, you say? Ha! As if I hadn't boosted them to Aunt Georgiana till my lips cracked. And with what result? So far, none. But wait till tonight."

"It is tonight."

"I mean, wait till later on tonight. Watch my little experiment."

"What little experiment?"

"Ah!"

"What do you mean, 'Ah'?"

"Just 'Ah!' " said Freddie.

The hour of the after-dinner coffee found Blandings Castle apparently an abode of peace. The superficial observer, peeping into the amber drawing-room through the french windows that led to the terrace, would have said that all was well with the inmates of this stately home of England. Lord Emsworth sat in a corner absorbed in a volume dealing with the treatment of pigs in sickness and in health. His sister, Lady Constance Keeble, was sewing. His other sister, Lady Alcester, was gazing at Gertrude. Gertrude was gazing at Orlo Watkins. And Orlo Watkins was gazing at the ceiling and singing in that crooning voice of his a song of Roses.

The Hon. Freddie Threepwood was not present. And that fact alone, if one may go by the views of his father, Lord Emsworth, should have been enough to make a success of any party.

And yet beneath this surface of cosy peace troubled currents were running. Lady Alcester, gazing at Gertrude, found herself a prey to gloom. She did not like the way Gertrude was gazing at Orlo Watkins. Gertrude, for her part, as the result of her recent conversation with the Hon. Freddie, was experiencing twinges of remorse and doubt. Lady Constance was still ruffled from the effect of Lady Alcester's sisterly frankness that evening on the subject of the imbecility of hostesses who deliberately let Crooning Tenors loose in castles. And Lord Emsworth was in that state of peevish exasperation which comes to dreamy old gentlemen who, wishing to read of Pigs, find their concentration impaired by voices singing of Roses.

Only Orlo Watkins was happy. And presently he, too, was to join the ranks of gloom. For just as he started to let himself go and handle this song as a song should be handled, there came from the other side of the door the sound of eager barking. A dog seemed to be without. And, apart from the fact that he disliked and feared all dogs, a tenor resents competition.

The next moment the door had opened, and the Hon. Freddie Threepwood appeared. He carried a small sack, and was accompanied by Bottles, the latter's manner noticeably lacking in response.

On the face of the Hon. Freddie, as he advanced into the room, there was that set, grim expression which is always seen on the faces of those who are about to put their fortune to the test, to win or lose it all. The Old Guard at Waterloo looked much the same. For Freddie had decided to stake all on a single throw.

Many young men in his position, thwarted by an aunt who resolutely declined to amble across to the stables and watch a dog redeem himself among the rats, would have resigned themselves sullenly to defeat. But Freddie was made of finer stuff.

"Aunt Georgiana," he said, holding up the sack, at which Bottles was making agitated leaps, "you refused to come to the stables this afternoon to watch this Donaldson's Dog-Joy-fed animal in action, so you have left me no alternative but to play the fixture on your own ground."

Lord Emsworth glanced up from his book.

"Frederick, stop gibbering. And take that dog out of here."

Lady Constance glanced up from her sewing.

"Frederick, if you are coming in, come in and sit down. And take that dog out of here."

Lady Alcester, glancing up from Gertrude, exhibited in even smaller degree the kindly cordiality which might have been expected from an aunt.

"Oh, do go away, Freddie! You're a perfect nuisance. And take that dog out of here."

The Hon. Freddie, with a noble look of disdain, ignored them all.

"I have here, Aunt Georgiana," he said, "a few simple rats. If you will kindly step out on to the terrace I shall be delighted to give a demonstration which should, I think, convince even your stubborn mind."

The announcement was variously received by the various members of the company. Lady Alcester screamed. Lady Constance sprang for the bell. Lord Emsworth snorted. Orlo Watkins blanched and retired behind Gertrude. And Gertrude, watching him blanch, seeing him retire, tightened her lips. A country-bred girl, she was on terms of easy familiarity with rats, and this evidence of alarm in one whom she had set on a pedestal disquieted her.

The door opened and Beach entered. He had come in pursuance of his regular duties to remove the coffee cups, but arriving, found other tasks assigned to him.

"Beach!" The voice was that of Lady Constance. "Take away those rats."

"Rats, m'lady?"

"Take that sack away from Mr. Frederick!"

Beach understood. If he was surprised at the presence of the younger son of the house in the amber drawing-room with a sack of rats in his hand, he gave no indication of the fact. With a murmured apology, he secured the sack and started to withdraw. It was not, strictly, his place to carry rats, but a good butler is always ready to give and take. Only so can the amenities of a large country house be preserved.

"And don't drop the dashed things," urged Lord Emsworth.

"Very good, m'lord."

The Hon. Freddie had flung himself into a chair, and was sitting with his chin cupped in his hands, a bleak look on his face. To an ardent young go-getter these tyrannous actions in restraint of trade are hard to bear.

Lord Emsworth returned to his book.

Lady Constance returned to her sewing.

Lady Alcester returned to her thoughts.

At the piano Orlo Watkins was endeavouring to justify the motives which had led him a few moments before to retire prudently behind Gertrude.

"I hate rats," he said. "They jar upon me."

"Oh?" said Gertrude.

"I'm not afraid of them, of course, but they give me the creeps."

"Oh?" said Gertrude.

There was an odd look in her eyes. Of what was she thinking, this idealistic girl? Was it of the evening, a few short weeks before, when, suddenly encountering a beastly bat in the gloaming, she had found in the Rev. Rupert Bingham a sturdy and intrepid protector? Was she picturing the Rev. Rupert as she had seen him then—gallant, fearless, cleaving the air with long sweeps of his clerical hat, encouraging her the while with word and gesture?

Apparently so, for a moment later she spoke.

"How are you on bats?"

"Rats?"

"Bats."

"Oh, bats?"

"Are you afraid of bats?"

"I don't like bats," admitted Orlo Watkins.

Then, dismissing the subject, he reseated himself at the piano and sang of June and the scent of unseen flowers.

Of all the little group in the amber drawing-room, only one member has now been left unaccounted for.

An animal of slow thought-processes, the dog Bottles had not

at first observed what was happening to the sack. At the
moment of its transference from the custody of Freddie to that
of Beach, it had been engaged in sniffing at the leg of a chair.
It was only as the door began to close that he became aware
of the bereavement that threatened him. He bounded forward
with a passionate cry, but it was too late. He found himself
faced by unyielding wood. And when he started to scratch
vehemently on this wood, a sharp pain assailed him. A book
on the treatment of Pigs in sickness and in health, superbly
aimed, had struck him. Then, for a space, he, like the Hon.
Freddie Threepwood, his social sponsor, sat down and mourned.

"Take that beastly, blasted, infernal dog out of here," cried
Lord Emsworth.

Freddie rose listlessly.

"It's old Beefers' dog," he said. "Beefers will be here at any
moment. We can hand the whole conduct of the affair over
to him."

Gertrude started.

"Is Rupert coming here tonight?"

"Said he would," responded Freddie, and passed from the
scene. He had had sufficient of his flesh and blood and was
indisposed to linger. It was his intention to pop down to
Market Blandings in his two-seater, soothe his wounded sensi-
bilities, so far as they were capable of being soothed, with a
visit to the local motion-picture house, look in at the Emsworth Arms for a spot of beer, and then home to bed, to forget.

Gertrude had fallen into a reverie. Her fair young face was
overcast. A feeling of embarrassment had come upon her.
When she had written that letter and posted it on the previous
night, she had not foreseen that the Rev. Rupert would be
calling so soon.

"I didn't know Rupert was coming tonight," she said.

"Oh, yes," said Lady Alcester brightly.

"Like a lingering tune, my whole life through, 'twill haunt

me for EV-ah, that night in June with you-oo," sang
Orlo Watkins.

And Gertrude, looking at him, was aware for the first time
of a curious sensation of not being completely in harmony
with this young, whiskered man. She wished he would stop
singing. He prevented her thinking.

Bottles, meanwhile, had resumed his explorations. Dogs are
philosophers. They soon forget. They do not waste time regret-
ting the might-have-beens. Adjusting himself with composure
to the changed conditions, Bottles moved to and fro in a spirit
of affable inquiry. He looked at Lord Emsworth, considered
the idea of seeing how he smelt, thought better of it, and
advanced towards the french windows. Something was rustling
in the bushes outside, and it seemed to him that this might
well be looked into before he went and breathed on Lady
Constance's leg.

He had almost reached his objective, when Lady Alcester's
Airedale, who had absented himself from the room some time
before in order to do a bit of bone-burying, came bustling in,
ready, his business completed, to resume the social whirl.

Seeing Bottles, he stopped abruptly.

Both then began a slow and cautious forward movement, of
a crab-like kind. Arriving at close quarters, they stopped again.
Their nostrils twitched a little. They rolled their eyes. And
to the ears of those present there came, faintly at first, a low,
throaty sound, like the far-off gargling of an octogenarian with
bronchial trouble.

This rose to a sudden crescendo. And the next moment hos-
tilities had begun.

In underrating Bottles's qualities and scoffing at him as a
fighting force, Lady Alcester had made an error. Capable
though he was of pusillanimity in the presence of female
Pekingese, there was nothing of the weakling about this sterling
animal. He had cleaned up every dog in Much Matchingham

and was spoken of on all sides—from the Blue Boar in the High Street to the distant Cow and Caterpillar on the Shrewsbury Road—as an ornament to the Vicarage and a credit to his master's Cloth.

On the present occasion, moreover, he was strengthened by the fact that he felt he had right on his side. In spite of a certain coldness on the part of the Castle circle and a soreness about the ribs where the book on Pigs and their treatment had found its billet, there seems to be no doubt that Bottles had by this time become thoroughly convinced that this drawing-room was his official home. And, feeling that all these delightful people were relying on him to look after their interests and keep alien and subversive influences at a distance, he advanced with a bright willingness to the task of ejecting this intruder.

Nor was the Airedale disposed to hold back. He, too, was no stranger to the ring. In Hyde Park, where, when at his London residence, he took his daily airing, he had met all comers and acquitted himself well. Dogs from Mayfair, dogs from Bayswater, dogs from as far afield as the Brompton Road and West Kensington had had experience of the stuff of which he was made. Bottles reminded him a little of an animal from Pont Street, over whom he had once obtained a decision on the banks of the Serpentine; and he joined battle with an easy confidence.

The reactions of a country-house party to an after-dinner dogfight in the drawing-room always vary considerably according to the individual natures of its members. Lady Alcester, whose long association with the species had made her a sort of honorary dog herself, remained tranquil. She surveyed the proceedings with unruffled equanimity through a tortoise-shell-rimmed lorgnette. Her chief emotion was one of surprise at the fact that Bottles was unquestionably getting the better of the exchanges. She liked his footwork. Impressed, she was obliged to admit that, if this was the sort of battler it turned out, there must be something in Donaldson's Dog-Joy after all.

The rest of the audience were unable to imitate her non-chalance. The two principals were giving that odd illusion, customary on these occasions, of being all over the place at the same time: and the demeanour of those in the ring-side seats was frankly alarmed. Lady Constance had backed against the wall, from which position she threw a futile cushion. Lord Emsworth, in his corner, was hunting feebly for ammunition and wishing that he had not dropped the pince-nez, without which he was no sort of use in a crisis.

And Gertrude? Gertrude was staring at Orlo Watkins, who, with a resource and presence of mind unusual in one so young, had just climbed on top of a high cabinet containing china.

His feet were level with her eyes; she saw they were feet of clay.

And it was at this moment, when a girl stood face to face with her soul, that the door opened.

"Mr. Bingham," announced Beach.

Men of the physique of the Rev. Rupert Bingham are not as a rule quick thinkers. From earliest youth, the Rev. Rupert had run to brawn rather than brain. But even the dullest-witted person could have told, on crossing that threshold, that there was a dogfight going on. Beefy Bingham saw it in a flash, and he acted promptly.

There are numerous methods of stopping these painful affairs. Some advocate squirting water, others prefer to sprinkle pepper. Good results may be obtained, so one school of thought claims, by holding a lighted match under the nearest nose. Beefy Bingham was impatient of these subtleties.

To Beefy all this was old stuff. Ever since he had been given his Cure of Souls, half his time, it sometimes seemed to him, had been spent in hauling Bottles away from the throats of the dogs of his little flock. Experience had given him a technique. He placed one hand on the neck of the Airedale, the other on the neck of Bottles, and pulled. There was a rending sound, and they came apart.

"Rupert!" cried Gertrude.

Gazing at him, she was reminded of the heroes of old. And few could have denied that he made a strangely impressive figure, this large young man, standing there with bulging eyes and a gyrating dog in each hand. He looked like a statue of Right triumphing over Wrong. You couldn't place it exactly, because it was so long since you had read the book, but he reminded you of something out of *Pilgrim's Progress*.

So, at least, thought Gertrude. To Gertrude it was as if the scales had fallen from her eyes and she had wakened from some fevered dream. Could it be she, she was asking herself, who had turned from this noble youth and strayed towards one who, though on the evidence he seemed to have a future before him as an Alpine climber, was otherwise so contemptible?

"Rupert!" said Gertrude.

Beefy Bingham had now completed his masterly campaign. He had thrown Bottles out of the window and shut it behind him. He had dropped the Airedale to the carpet, where it now sat, licking itself in a ruminative way. He had produced a handkerchief and was passing it over his vermilion brow.

"Oh, Rupert!" said Gertrude, and flung herself into his arms.

The Rev. Rupert said nothing. On such occasions your knowledgeable Vicar does not waste words.

Nor did Orlo Watkins speak. He had melted away. Perhaps, perched on his eyrie, he had seen in Gertrude's eyes the look which, when seen in the eyes of a girl by any interested party, automatically induces the latter to go to his room and start packing, in readiness for the telegram which he will receive on the morrow, summoning him back to London on urgent business. At any rate, he had melted.

It was late that night when the Hon. Freddie Threepwood

returned to the home of his fathers. Moodily undressing, he was surprised to hear a knock on the door.

His Aunt Georgiana entered. On her face was the unmistakable look of a mother whose daughter has seen the light and will shortly be marrying a deserving young clergyman with a bachelor uncle high up in the shipping business.

"Freddie," said Lady Alcester, "you know that stuff you're always babbling about—I've forgotten its name . . ."

"Donaldson's Dog-Joy," said Freddie. "It may be obtained either in the small (or one-and-threepenny) packets or in the half-crown (or large) size. A guarantee goes with each purchase. Unique in its health-giving properties . . ."

"I'll take two tons to start with," said Lady Alcester.

elliott erwitt's dogs

Trouville, France

Prague, Czechoslovakia

New York City,
New York

Paris, France

New York City, New York

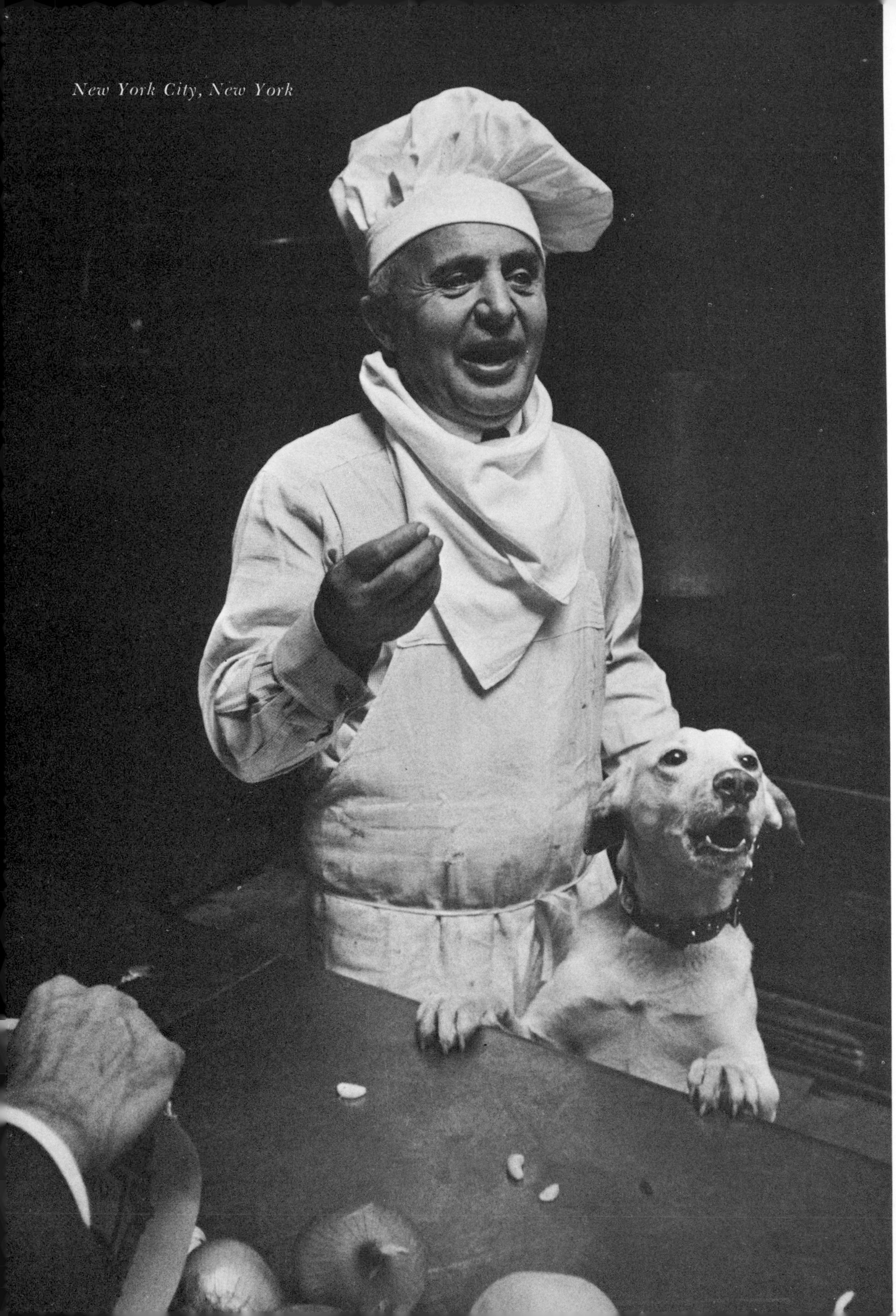

Dublin, Ireland

Cambridge, Massachusetts

the dog noble

from *Eyes and Ears*

HENRY WARD BEECHER

The first summer which we spent in Lenox, we had along a very intelligent dog, named Noble. He was learned in many things, and by his dog-lore excited the undying admiration of all the children. But there were some things which Noble could never learn. Having on one occasion seen a red squirrel run into a hole in a stone wall, he could not be persuaded that he was not there for evermore.

Several red squirrels lived close to the house, and had become familiar, but not tame. They kept up a regular romp with Noble. They would come down from the maple-trees with provoking coolness; they would run along the fence almost within reach; they would cock their tails and sail across the road to the barn; and yet there was such a well-timed calculation under all this apparent rashness that Noble invariably arrived at the critical spot just as the squirrel left it.

On one occasion Noble was so close upon his red-backed friend that, unable to get up the maple-tree, he dodged into a hole in the wall, ran through the chinks, emerged at a little distance, and sprung into the tree. The intense enthusiasm of the dog at that hole can hardly be described. He filled it full of barking. He pawed and scratched as if undermining a bastion. Standing off at a little distance, he would pierce the

hole with a gaze as intense and fixed as if he were trying mag-
netism on it. Then, with tail extended, and every hair there-
on electrified, he would rush at the empty hole with a prodigi-
ous onslaught.

This imaginary squirrel haunted Noble night and day. The
very squirrel himself would run up before his face into the
tree, and, crouched in a crotch, would sit silently watching the
whole process of bombarding the empty hole, with great sobri-
ety and relish. But Noble would allow of no doubts. His conviction that the hole had a squirrel in it continued unshaken
for six weeks. When all other occupations failed, this hole
remained to him. When there were no more chickens to harry,
no pigs to bite, no cattle to chase, no children to romp with,
no expeditions to make with the grown folks, and when he
had slept all that his dogskin would hold, he would walk out
of the yard, yawn and stretch himself, and then look wistfully
at the hole, as if thinking to himself, "Well, as there is nothing else to do, I may as well try that hole again!"

dog

WILLIAM JAY SMITH

Dogs are quite a bit like people,
   Or so it seems to me somehow.
Like people, Dogs go anywhere,
They swim in the sea, they leap through the air,
They bark and growl, they sit and stare,
They even wear what people wear.
Look at that Poodle with a hat on its noodle,
Look at that Boxer with a long silver-fox fur,
Look at that Whippet in its calico tippet,
Look at that Sealyham in diamonds from Rotterdam,
Look at that Afghan wrapped in an afghan,
Look at that Chow down there on a dhow
All decked out for some big powwow
With Pekinese waiting to come kowtow.
   Don't they all look just like people?
   People you've *seen* somewhere? Bowwow!

something of a borzoi

D. D. PORTER

Ever since the age of three when I had a contretemps among
the table legs with my grandmother's Sealyham—a question of
territorial rights—my feelings about dogs have been rather
more than mixed. But in spite of the memory of those needle
teeth that punctured the lobe of my pink, infant ear I had,
until two years ago, been unwilling to pass final judgment on
a whole race. The incident that caused me to come down off
the fence about dogs in general on the side of the Anti-Canine
Defense League occurred while I was spending a bewildered
postgraduate year in France, where, it must be said, dogs generally know their place. I was employed as an assistant in a
school and required to talk English for twelve hours a week
—one of those sinecures that soured as the year wore on and
opposition hardened into truculent anti-British feeling. By
the beginning of January I had come to discover that the main-
tenance allowance I received did just that; it maintained me
and afforded me my daily bread. For the occasional nibble at
life's fruitcake, not to speak of its icing sugar, I would have to
look elsewhere. It was thus that I went in search of private
lessons and made up my mind once and for all about dogs.

A friend of a friend made it known to me that a wealthy
bourgeois family was very anxious to find someone to give

120

English conversation lessons to their son. For this I would receive six hundred francs a time and lunch. All I had to do was to talk English to the boy while we ate. Veiled, third-hand promises were breathed into my ear about Easter holidays in their villa at Cap Ferrat, and the outlines of a nubile daughter with too much time on her hands were sketched in.

I was living during that particularly severe winter in a large, high-ceilinged bedroom facing north that I had chosen on account of its coolness on one late autumn day of dusty heat. For heating there was a single, narrow radiator. With the snow piled up on the sill outside I would crouch there, embracing its four slim, silver bars that were never more than lukewarm and abandon myself to elaborate, fantasy visions of heat and food. On the evening of the tenth of January I shivered myself to sleep, curled up womb fashion in one corner of the white waste of my vast double bed, promising myself that the next day would mark a turning point in my experience of France. At lunchtime on that day I was to present myself for the first time for lunch and conversation.

At a quarter to twelve that morning I sprang out of bed and threw on all the clothes I had taken off the previous night before I was cut down by the cold air. Trousers, shirt, two sweaters, jacket and overcoat. Socks, shoes and overshoes followed before I proceeded to the trying business of shaving at speed in ice-cold water. My lunch was at twelve and I had to get to the other side of town. By the time I had finished shaving there was blood and water on my collar and only half my face was smooth.

It was a little after half past twelve when I found the house in a *"quartier chic"* two doors up from the Spanish Consulate. It seemed very like an eighteenth-century "hotel," gray and very French in a sparely elegant way. All the shutters were down and it had that forbidding, gone-away-for-the-duration look of so many French houses. I rang and waited suspiciously

—I'd had trouble from Continental doors before. But this door
was conventional enough. It opened finally from the inside
and I was faced across the opening with a shriveled and diminu-
tive figure in black. We considered each other in silence for a
time while I rapidly tried to put together a sentence in French.
But she got there first.

"Vous désirez, Monsieur?" She looked up at me through one
sallow and heavy-lidded eye that peered out at me like a water
rat from its hole in a riverbank.

I drew a breath and started to explain, winding myself into
one of those foreign sentences that proliferate endlessly away
from me. I was the friend of a friend of the gentleman who
was acquainted with the lady of the house and who had said
that the *"fils"* of the lady of the—*"Fils,"* she echoed. The word
seemed to puzzle her.

"Fils," I repeated firmly—it was a word that I was sure I
knew—and gestured in the air patting an imaginary head some
three feet above the pavement. She watched my activity with
narrow-eyed interest, then fixed me again with her probing,
slightly malevolent eye. Her other eye looked a good deal
kinder, dimmed with age and greater understanding.

I decided to change my approach.

"Anglais," I insisted, thumping my chest. *"Moi Anglais."*

Much to my surprise that turned out to be excessively funny,
for she broke into wheezy, cracked laughter that left me open-
mouthed and anxious for her health.

"Boche, moi Boche," she said and collapsed against the door-
jamb. She was obviously finding it difficult to do justice to the
humor of the situation and get all the air she needed at the
same time. Then she began to cough, and two tears detached
themselves slowly from her eyelids and meandered down corrugated, brown-paper cheeks.

I stepped inside the house and gave her a few tentative pats on the back. It was like handling my sister's baby; I was afraid that something might cave in or come away in my hands. Somehow I armed her to a seat in the vestibule.

"*Moi, Boche,*" she repeated and raised a quivering skinny arm in what I took to be a Nazi salute.

"*Oui, oui,*" I said, nodding. Humor them, that's all you have to do, humor them. But she seemed to have taken to me, I saw with relief, and kept winking and shaking her head at me in a droll, knowing way.

"*Vous êtes invité par Monsieur?*" she finally asked from the gritty depths of her throat. She looked up at me, her little whiskered mouth puckered in a question.

"*Par Madame,*" I corrected her, keeping my left-hand, unshaven cheek averted from the black gimlet of that right eye. That too was found hilarious.

"*Venez Monsieur,*" she said, getting up and giving me a knowing jab in the stomach with her elbow. "*Venez. Il faut attendre. Vous êtes trop tôt.*"

"*Trop tôt.*" It was my turn to do the echoing. "*Trop tard,*" I said in surprise.

She had to hold on to the banisters at that. I began to warm to her. Even my rarest, premeditated *mots* had never drawn this response.

She led me through the thickly carpeted hall that was hung with tapestries for most of its length. Opening wide glass doors, she motioned me forward into a spacious drawing room at the far end of which was a dining recess. The table was laid for about a dozen people, I noticed with surprise. Cut glass and gleaming silver and cool white table linen were reflected in the dark glowing polish of the tabletop. This wasn't at all what I had expected. I thought in a moment of panic that I had better contract a headache and get out as fast as I could. But there were wonderful French culinary smells wafting in from the kitchen and I'd had no breakfast. I was also more than a little nervous of the effect of such a sudden announcement on my ancient friend.

"Asseyez-vous." She indicated some chairs placed round a low coffee table. Then she went out of another door shaking her head and muttering to herself. *"Par Madame,"* I heard her say with a chuckle.

The room was furnished with contemporary furniture of the most elegant and expensive kind; bucket chairs, a curving TV settee, standard lamps with delicate, swanlike necks, thick, white sheepskin rugs on the light-stained floor. Everything had been chosen with care and disposed by someone with an exceptional taste for interior decoration. There was a box of cigarettes on the coffee table and the art magazine, *L'Oeil*. A picture on the wall, a livid snowscape of a sad provincial church, caught my eye. It was, I noticed, a Utrillo.

This, I felt, shedding my coat, was my spiritual home. I strolled about savoring the temperate air of this living room, so redolent of gracious, moneyed ease. It was occurring to me with increasingly persuasive force that they might well have a spare room and that they would find my English conversation so obviously beneficial to their son that they would beg me to move in as house tutor. Warmth and just a little life-enhancing luxury and highly cultivated conversation. This at last was the *real* France that I was discovering. A studio with a sun lounge on the top floor and weekends of water skiing in their villa at the coast. The possibilities seemed endless. I tried three of the chairs in turn—there was one wooden chair in my own gaunt igloo—and finally settled for an off-white bucket model that sumptuously embraced me as I lowered myself into it. Helping myself to a cigarette, I sat back to prepare appropriately gracious, witty sallies that I would produce with casual *savoir faire* over lunch. Each course would be highlighted by a sparklingly turned phrase that would rock them on their slender chairs.

I was about to start in on the soup when the glass door that
the old lady had left ajar was pushed open and a large dog
loped massively into the room. It was one of the largest dogs
that I had ever seen, and it seemed to me to have something of
a borzoi about it, although there was a good deal of alien,
Western blood. I saw at a glance that it was one of nature's
comedians with shaggy ends of hair falling across its eyes, and
ears that stuck up as if it were listening in permanently delighted surprise to a rich orchestration of rare sounds—that
was my first impression at least. I realize now that had I looked
closer I would have detected the peeping malignity behind
those shaggy brows. It was a young animal, just about fully
grown but still at the stage when it was taken unawares by
unexpected, independent activity in its limbs.

It pulled up sharply when it saw me, then approached, pro-
prietary and suspicious and just a little anxious, padding forward on huge paws. It stopped again about two feet away and
gave a qualified, introductory growl, neither friendly nor threat-
ening but prepared to go either way. I was ready by this time
to greet even the least influential member of the houshold as
an old friend whom only time and a regretful dalliance in
life's byways had prevented me from meeting sooner.

"*Ça va, mon vieux,*" I said cordially, flicking ash toward
the ashtray. And I held out a tentative hand. Perhaps the
accent was wrong or the tone was found too patronizing. I
don't know, but he remained motionless, nose slightly elevated,
tail stuck out stiffly behind him. For the first time in my life
I knew what it was like to be an old mother partridge and
to be pointed. I considered him carefully.

"*Tu es gentil, hein?*" It was a Gallic interrogative that I
had perfected with no slight effort, and it struck me as the
most authentically native thing I could do—except possibly for
my indignantly expostulatory *Bah oui*, accompanied by a massive shift of the shoulders—if that wouldn't reassure him nothing else I could do would. Fortunately it seemed to work, for

with a few wags of the tail he advanced toward the proffered hand, sniffed it for a moment, seemed more than satisfied and took to licking. I was relieved and abandoned my hand to him completely. He started to make playful little snaps at it and I warmed to the game. He was, I felt sure, well able to distinguish between the play situation and reality, and I was expecting that at any moment someone would come walking in. What could be more likely to set up an immediate bond of sympathy with any member of the family than to be found on affectionate terms with their dog? I already had half a sentence in my head, *"J'ai déjà fait la connaissance . . .,"* and was searching round for an adequate epithet to add a clinching touch of humor. But no one came.

I wondered where the old lady had gone to, as I could no longer hear her pottering about in what I thought was the kitchen. I presumed she had at last gone to tell someone that I had arrived. My left hand was growing increasingly sticky and the dog, far from getting tired of alternately licking and gnawing playfully, began to get more excited. Suddenly he decided that it would be more fun on the floor and rolled over on his back, trying to persuade me to join him down there by tugging at my sleeve with his teeth. I declined, however, and shook myself free. In spite of everything I was beginning to feel a little put out. After all, if I was half an hour late that was no reason to leave me to fight off the dog for half an hour.

I picked up the magazine and opened it with a huffy crackle. I hoped that he would feel snubbed and understand that the game was now over and that we were going to sit down quietly. I waited with the magazine held in front of my face expecting to hear the sound of his retreating footsteps. But there was silence. After a few more moments I allowed my curiosity to get the better of me and slowly lowering the paper peeped over the top. It was a blunder that proved fatal. He was lying flat on his side with one front paw tucked in against his body. He stared up at me with one ear bent forward and his mouth slightly open. His whole body was coiled with the alert expectancy of a spring. As soon as our eyes met, his tail thumped against the floor and he made a swoop for my shoe, assuming that the break was over and we were now entering the next, more active session. I went back behind the magazine again but he saw that merely as a feint now and continued snuffling at my light-toned suèdes. He finally got the whole shoe in his jaw. I jerked it free, tucking my leg up under me on the chair. He went straight for my other foot. I withdrew that too. Scrambling onto his feet, he came on after me into the chair, suddenly wanting to lick my face. My cigarette dropped from my mouth. I tried pushing him off with one hand while I groped for my cigarette with the other, but he was too heavy. Squeezing out from under him, I dropped over the side. The cigarette had slipped down into the chair next to the arm.

"*Va, idiot, va,*" I hurled at him, losing my precarious grip on the language in my excitement. Smoke was rising from the chair, so I tried stuffing my hand down to get at the cigarette. The dog was butting me from behind. I burned the tip of my finger and let out a yell. The cigarette slipped farther down into the chair.

"*Va, sacré borzoi, va. Les jeux sont faits.*"

I looked round wildly. There was no water on the table, but there were two bottles of wine. I looked back at the chair. The volume of smoke was increasing. Suddenly seized with panic, I rushed across and grabbed up one of the bottles of wine and, turning, wrenched out the cork with my teeth. Holding my hand over the top of the bottle, I stuffed it head foremost down in the chair and removed my hand. There was a distant hissing as of air running out of a punctured tire and a valedictory puff of smoke and the panic was over. I noticed that Borzoi was standing to one side wagging his tail and watching my movements with what in a human being might be accurately described as enthusiastic *Schadenfreude*. I licked at a trickle of wine on my chin and surveyed the contours of the off-white bucket. There were three astonishingly symmetrical circles of plum-colored Médoc on the seat at the front about the size of half crowns and a blotchy patch at the back that reminded me of a particularly disfiguring birthmark. I saw at a glance that nothing short of a skin graft could be done about the birthmark, so I transferred a cushion from another chair and reconsidered the half crowns. I looked in my pocket for a handkerchief but I had come out in such a hurry that I was without one. Plunging my hand into my trousers, I came up again with a shirttail that to a stranger's eye would have appeared curiously mutilated. The crenelated effect, however, had a simple explanation. It was from the tail that my mother, a thrifty soul, invariably carried off her supplies of patches for more exposed sections of my wilting shirts. I had remonstrated at length with her over the practice especially at a time when I was called upon to strip almost daily for a bout of athletic activity in the company of some sixty searching juvenile eyes (counting two for each head). Lately I had given up trying.

I spat on the tail and set to work on the chair. After some five minutes of spitting and rubbing I had to admit that progress was negligible, so I sat down on a sheepskin rug on the floor to rethink the situation. I took a swig at the bottle of wine which was little more than half full. I was about to raise the bottle a second time when I felt a humid blast of hot air on the back of my neck, followed by a damp tongue, just above the collar of my shirt, where I was conscious of needing a haircut.

"That's enough jokes for one day, joker," I said, getting to my feet, reassured by the masterful sound of my native idiom. The animal seemed impressed, too, for he stopped grinning —there's no other word for it, he was grinning all right—and allowed himself to be dragged across the floor by the long hair of his neck. He had no collar. I got him to the kitchen door and was about to push him through exultantly when I caught sight of a heap of meat lying within easy reach on a table. I stopped thoughtfully. I would probably survive the episode with the wine in the family's esteem but should I allow that large hunk of choice steak to be devoured by the dog, I would almost certainly alienate irreparably the affections of this one French family. There was nothing for it; we had to cohabit further, my scurrilous canine and I. But the free activity period was at an end as far as I was concerned. Something had to be done about those wine stains and quickly before someone came in and discovered me strolling about in their living room with a tattered shirttail hanging out of the front of my trousers. And I was determined that no dog was going to sabotage my chances of a life of ease.

Still holding tight to a handful of loose skin and hair, I looked about for a cord of some kind. But there was nothing in sight. Nothing. Then my eyes lighted on the curtain cord. It was stout enough, I thought, measuring it against his neck. I dragged him across to the window and fixed it round his neck. I think he had an idea of my intentions for he tried to resist, but I had a good grip on him and I was firm.

Having disposed of one problem, I returned at my leisure to consider how the half crowns were to be eliminated. Then I had it. Bread, bread and salt. Bread and salt get out ink, so why not wine? I transported a large plateful of chunky slices of French bread and the saltcellar from the table and, sitting down on the floor next to the chair, set to work. I sprinkled the three spots liberally with salt; then, spitting on my shirttail, rubbed hard. It was with something approaching exultation that I established that there were pinky stains on my tail. Then I turned to the bread, setting to work with a will at breaking off small lumps and rubbing until the lumps had crumbled away beneath my fingers.

I worked my way through half the plateful until the chair and the floor around it were powdered with fine crumbs and there was a small heap of crusts on the sheepskin rug. Progress was slow but I was convinced that it was being made as I sat there humming away to myself, thoroughly absorbed in the work in hand. Then for the second time within half an hour I permitted myself an unguarded gesture that brought disaster in its wake.

In a thoughtless moment as I straightened up from my work, I waved with careless bonhomie at Borzoi. He had been showing increasing dissatisfaction with his situation for some time, so, interpreting my nod as a sign that he had returned to favor, he bounded toward me, stopping briefly as he took up the slack in the cord. Resistance was momentary and then he was beside me trailing the whole window blind in his wake. The coffee table was brushed aside and delicate pink blooms spilled out of splintered faïence onto the floor. The bottle of wine rolled over and Médoc flooded across the sheepskin rug.

That, as far as I was concerned, was that, I decided, getting to my feet and brushing crumbs from my knees. A rudimentary handyman at the best of times, I recognized that things had now reached such a magnitude that I was quite out of my class. Careless of the consequences, I bundled Borzoi out into the kitchen, blind and everything, and donned my coat. I would leave a note saying that I had been called away but that I would explain everything—I reckoned it would take me a week's work, but I was younger then and I thought that it might at least be done.

I looked round for writing materials. I had a pen but there had been no ink in it for several weeks past. Short of penetrating drawers, which my inherited sense of delicacy prevented me from doing, there was nothing to write on or with as far as I could see. I improvised. Filling my pen from a pool of Médoc '55, I spread out a paper serviette and wrote the following note with a spidery hand:

Je suis très, très chagriné mais la leçon n'aura pas lieu. Je suis appellé très urgentement. Je vous expliquerai la cause des ravages terribles. C'était la faute du méchant chien. La servante avec la robe noire est disparue dans la cuisine. Je vous prie de croire à ma parfaite consideration.*

The last sentence I knew was entirely correct. I had copied it from a dictionary once and with it had finished every letter that I have ever written in French. I appended a signature that was satisfactorily illegible and picking up half a dozen cigarettes and a piece of Camembert, I left—I felt they were owing to me; after all, I had been invited to lunch. The last things I heard as I stealthily let myself out the front door were whines and scratching sounds coming from the kitchen.

It was about three days afterward that I received a letter wondering why I had not come to lunch the week before and whether I would be coming the following week. I had, it appeared, got the address wrong. I never went back to the other house to explain what happened—you may call it moral cowardice if you wish and I accept the censure—so I don't know what their reactions were. They probably thought an illiterate half-wit had broken in, deliberately smashed the place up and tried to hang their dog.

---

* I am very, very sorry but the lesson will not take place. I have been called away very urgently. I will explain the reason for this terrible destruction. It was the fault of the wretched dog. The servant with the black dress disappeared into the kitchen. Please be assured of my kindest regards.

larry's dog

our dumb friends

RALPH WOTHERSPOON

My home is a haven for one who enjoys
The clamor of children and ear-splitting noise
From a number of dogs who are always about,
And who want to come in and, once in, to go out.
Whenever I settle to read by the fire,
Some dog will develop an urge to retire,
And I'm constantly opening and shutting the door
For a dog to depart or, as mentioned before,
For a dog to arrive who, politely admitted,
Will make a bee-line for the chair I've just quitted,
Our friends may be dumb, but my house is a riot,
Where I cannot sit still and can never be quiet.

the low state
of whippet racing

from *Inside Benchley*

ROBERT BENCHLEY

It does not seem too soon now to begin formulating plans for next year's whippet racing. While there are still a few more races on the 1928 schedule, most of the important ones have been run off and the leading whippets have practically all broken training.

Whippet racing in recent years has deteriorated into a sordid spectacle, productive only of gigantic gate receipts for the promoters. At one whippet race on Long Island last summer, it is estimated that forty people lined the course, and, as each of these forty paid something in the neighborhood of a quarter for parking their cars in a nearby field, it will be seen that the thing has already got out of hand and is now in the class of mad sport carnivals.

This has naturally had its reaction on the whippets themselves. They have become mercenary and callous. All they think of is money, money, money. The idea of sport for sport's sake is a dream of the past as far as whippets are concerned. In order to make the game what it used to be, we shall have to bring up a whole new breed of whippets and send the present success-crazed organization out on the road in circuses where they may indulge their lust for gain without hindrance of any considerations of sportsmanship.

Perhaps a few examples may serve to illustrate my point. I witnessed a whippet race in California recently at which the gate happened to be very small. There had been no publicity worthy of the name and the word had simply got around among the racetrack gang that some whippets were going to race at three o'clock. This brought out a crowd of perhaps six people, exclusive of the owners and trainers. Four of the six were chance passers-by and the other two were state policemen.

Now evidently the small size of the crowd enraged the whippets or, at any rate, threw them into such a state of mind that they gave up all idea of racing and took to kidding. In the first place they were not halfway down the lanes when two of them stopped and walked back, while the other two began wrestling good-naturedly. The owners at the finish line called frantically, but to no avail, and the race had to be called off.

In the second race they would not even start. When the gun was fired, they turned as if by pre-arranged mutiny and began jumping up and kissing their trainers. This race also had to be called off.

By this time the crowd was in an ugly humor and one or two started to boo. The state police, scenting trouble, went

home. This left four spectators and further upset the whippets. A conference of the owners and trainers resulted in what you might call practically nothing. It got along toward supper time and even I went home. I looked in the papers the next morning but could find no news of the races, so I gathered that the rest of the heats had been called off too.

This pretty well indicates the state in which whippet racing now finds itself in this country. The remedy is up to those of us old whippet fanciers who have the time and the means to reform the thing from the ground up.

First, I would recommend a revision of the system of whippet-calling. As you no doubt know, a whippet race is at least one-third dependent on calling. The trainer leads the whippet from the finish line up the lane to the starting point (a silly procedure to begin with) and then holds him in leash until the gun. The owner, or some close personal friend, stands at

the finish line and calls to the whippet, which is supposed to drive him crazy and make him run like mad back down the lane again in a desire to reach his owner. As we have seen, the whippet can take it or leave it and is by no means certain to show any desire at all to get back to the caller. Now this must be due to the calling. If the thing were made attractive

at all for the whippet to reach the finish line, we would see no more of this hopping up and kissing trainers at the start.

As near as I could distinguish, most of the owners called out, "Come on, Luke!" or "Here, Bennie, here!" Now obviously there was nothing very exciting about these calls. You and I wouldn't run like mad down a lane to get to someone who was calling, "Come on, Charlie!" or "Here, Bob, here!"

There must be some more attractive sounds made to entice the whippets down the lanes. Not knowing exactly what it is that whippets like best, it is a little difficult for me to make suggestions. I don't know and I don't pretend to know. All I am sure of is that the whippets aren't particularly attracted by what is being held out to them now.

Now in the matter of blankets. On the way up the lanes to the starting point, the whippets are forced to wear blankets like race horses. This saps not only their vitality but their self-respect. It is all right for a race horse to wear a blanket if he wants to, because he is big and can carry it off well. But when you get a whippet who, even with everything showing, can hardly be seen unless you have him in your lap, and then cover him up in a blanket, it just makes a nance out of him, that's all. They look like so many trotting blankets, and they must know it. A whippet has feelings as well as the rest of us. You can't make a dog ashamed to appear in public and then expect him to run a race. As it stands, they are so ashamed of their blankets that they have to do something on the way down the lanes to appear virile. So they stop right in the middle of the race and wrestle.

This wrestling business calls for attention, too. It is all right for dogs to kid, but they don't have to do it in the middle of a race. It is as if Charlie Paddock, while running the hundred, should stop after about fifty yards and push one of his opponents playfully on the shoulder and say, "Last tag!" and then as if his opponent should stop and chase Charlie around in the track trying to tag him back. What kind of time would they make in a race like that?

I don't think that the thing has ever been put up to the whippets quite frankly in this manner. If someone could take a few whippets to a track meet and (the whole gag having been worked up before, of course, among the runners) the thing should deteriorate into a rough-and-tumble clowning match of pushing and hauling one another, the whippets might see what it looks like. You could say to them: "Now you see, that's how *you* look when you stop in the middle of a race and wrestle all over the track." They would be pretty ashamed, I should think.

The less said about their jumping up and kissing their trainers at the start, the better. This is something that a good psychoanalyst ought to handle. But so long as it is allowed to go on, whippet racing will be in the doldrums. And so long as whippet racing is in the doldrums—well, it is in the doldrums, that's all.

Better in the doldrums, say I, than for the whippets to so far forget the principles of good, clean amateur sport as to pursue a mechanical rabbit.

Illustrated by Gluyas Williams

montmorency

from *Three Men in a Boat*

JEROME K. JEROME

To look at Montmorency you would imagine that he was an angel sent upon the earth, for some reason withheld from mankind, in the shape of a small fox-terrier. There is a sort of Oh—what—a—wicked—world—this—is—and—how—I—wish—I—could—do—something—to—make—it—better—and—nobler expression about Montmorency that has been known to bring the tears into the eyes of pious old ladies and gentlemen.

When first he came to live at my expense, I never thought I should be able to get him to stop long. I used to sit down and look at him, as he sat on the rug and looked up at me, and think: "Oh, that dog will never live. He will be snatched up to the bright skies in a chariot, that is what will happen to him."

But, when I had paid for about a dozen chickens that he had killed; and had dragged him, growling and kicking, by the scruff of his neck, out of a hundred and fourteen street fights; and had had a dead cat brought round for my inspection by an irate female, who called me a murderer; and had been summoned by the man next door but one for having a ferocious dog at large, that had kept him pinned up in his own toolshed, afraid to venture his nose outside the door for over two hours on a cold night; and had learned that the gardener, unknown to myself, had won thirty shillings by backing him to kill rats against time, then I began to think that maybe they'd let him remain on earth for a bit longer, after all.

The only subject on which Montmorency and I have any serious difference of opinion is cats. I like cats; Montmorency does not.

When I meet a cat, I say, "Poor Pussy!" and stoop down and tickle the side of its head; and the cat sticks up its tail in a rigid, cast-iron manner, arches its back, and wipes its nose up against my trousers; and all is gentleness and peace. When Montmorency meets a cat, the whole street knows about it; and there is enough bad language wasted in ten seconds to last an ordinary respectable man all his life, with care.

I do not blame the dog (contenting myself, as a rule, with merely clouting his head or throwing stones at him), because I take it that it is his nature. Fox-terriers are born with about four times as much original sin in them as other dogs are, and it will take years and years of patient effort on the part of us Christians to bring about any appreciable reformation in the rowdiness of the fox-terrier nature.

I remember being in the lobby of the Haymarket Stores one day, and all round about me were dogs, waiting for the return of their owners, who were shopping inside. There were a mastiff, and one or two collies, and a St. Bernard, a few retrievers and Newfoundlands, a boar-hound, a French poodle, with plenty of hair round its head, but mangy about the middle; a bulldog, a few Lowther Arcade sort of animals, about the size of rats, and a couple of Yorkshire tykes.

There they sat, patient, good, and thoughtful. A solemn peacefulness seemed to reign in that lobby. An air of calmness and resignation—of gentle sadness pervaded the room.

Then a sweet young lady entered, leading a meek-looking little fox-terrier, and left him, chained up there, between the

bulldog and the poodle. He sat and looked about him for a
minute. Then he cast up his eyes to the ceiling, and seemed,
judging from his expression, to be thinking of his mother.
Then he yawned. Then he looked round at the other dogs,
all silent, grave, and dignified.

He looked at the bulldog, sleeping dreamlessly on his right.
He looked at the poodle, erect and haughty, on his left. Then,
without a word of warning, without the shadow of a provoca-
tion, he bit that poodle's near foreleg, and a yelp of agony
rang through the quiet shades of that lobby.

The result of his first experiment seemed highly satisfactory
to him, and he determined to go on and make things lively
all round. He sprang over the poodle and vigorously attacked
a collie, and the collie woke up, and immediately commenced
a fierce and noisy contest with the poodle. Then Foxey came
back to his own place, and caught the bulldog by the ear, and
tried to throw him away; and the bulldog, a curiously impar-
tial animal, went for everything he could reach, including the
hall-porter, which gave that dear little terrier the opportunity
to enjoy an uninterrupted fight of his own with an equally
willing Yorkshire tyke.

Anyone who knows canine nature need hardly be told that,
by this time, all the other dogs in the place were fighting as
if their hearths and homes depended on the fray. The big dogs
fought each other indiscriminately; and the little dogs fought
among themselves, and filled up their spare time by biting the
legs of the big dogs.

The whole lobby was a perfect pandemonium, and the din
was terrific. A crowd assembled outside in the Haymarket, and
asked if it was a vestry meeting; or, if not, who was being murdered, and why? Men came with poles and ropes, and tried to
separate the dogs, and the police were sent for.

And in the midst of the riot that sweet young lady returned,
and snatched up that sweet little dog of hers (he had laid

the tyke up for a month, and had on the expression, now, of a
new-born lamb) into her arms, and kissed him, and asked him
if he was killed, and what those great nasty brutes of dogs had
been doing to him; and he nestled up against her, and gazed
up into her face with a look that seemed to say: "Oh, I'm so
glad you've come to take me away from this disgraceful scene!"

She said that the people at the stores had no right to allow
great savage things like those other dogs to be put with respectable people's dogs, and that she had a great mind to summon
somebody.

Such is the nature of fox-terriers; and, therefore, I do not
blame Montmorency for his tendency to row with cats, but he
wished he had not given way to it that morning.

We were, as I have said, returning from a dip, and half-way
up the High Street a cat darted out from one of the houses in
front of us, and began to trot across the road. Montmorency
gave a cry of joy—the cry of a stern warrior who sees his enemy
given over to his hands—the sort of cry Cromwell might have
uttered when the Scots came down the hill—and flew after
his prey.

His victim was a large black tom. I never saw a larger cat, nor
a more disreputable-looking cat. It had lost half its tail, one of
its ears, and a fairly appreciable proportion of its nose. It was
a long, sinewy-looking animal. It had a calm, contented air
about it.

Montmorency went for that poor cat at the rate of twenty
miles an hour; but the cat did not hurry up—did not seem to
have grasped the idea that its life was in danger. It trotted
quietly on until its would-be assassin was within a yard of it,
and then it turned round and sat down in the middle of the
road, and looked at Montmorency with a gentle, inquiring
expression, that said:

"Yes? You want me?"

Montmorency does not lack pluck; but there was something

about the look of that cat that might have chilled the heart of
the boldest dog. He stopped abruptly, and looked back at Tom.

Neither spoke; but the conversation that one could imagine
was clearly as follows:

THE CAT: "Can I do anything for you?"

MONTMORENCY: "No—no, thanks."

THE CAT: "Don't you mind speaking, if you really want anything, you know."

MONTMORENCY *(backing down the High Street)*: "Oh no—
not at all—certainly—don't you trouble. I—I am afraid
I've made a mistake. I thought I knew you. Sorry I disturbed you."

THE CAT: "Not at all—quite a pleasure. Sure you don't want
anything, now?"

MONTMORENCY *(still backing)*: "Not at all, thanks—not at all
—very kind of you. Good morning."

THE CAT: "Good morning."

Then the cat rose, and continued his trot; and Montmorency, fitting what he calls his tail carefully into its groove,
came back to us, and took up an unimportant position in the
rear.

To this day, if you say the word "Cats!" to Montmorency, he
will visibly shrink and look up piteously at you, as if to say:

"Please don't."

one way to raise a pup

1

2

3

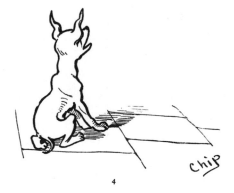

4

CHIP

a story with a sudden windup

CHIP

flurry at the
sheep dog trial

from *Sam Small Flies Again*

ERIC KNIGHT

The wind came clear over the great flat part of the moor near
Soderby. The gusts eddied, tearing away wisps of smell—the
smell of men packed in knots, of sheep, of trampled heath
grass. The size of the flatland made the noises small—the sharp
barks of dogs, the voices of men speaking in deep dialect.

The men of the different sections stood in separate knots.
Those from Polkingthorpe were ranged about Sam, their eyes
on him trustingly, half fearfully, as if they were a little awed
by what they had done, and the size of the bets they had made
from village loyalty.

"Now, Sam," Gaffer Sitherthwick mumbled slowly, "tha's
sure she can do it? For Ah've put up one pound again' two
pound ten that she's the winner."

"Now hold up, Gaffer," Capper Wambley wavered. "Tha
must remember she's never been really trained as a shepherd;
but what Ah say is, the way Sam's trained her this past week
she'll do owt he tells her best she can. And best ye can do is
best, as any man'll agree."

"Thankee, Capper," Sam acknowledged. "Now, lads, if ye
don't mind, Ah'd like to give her sort of secret instructions—
and calm her down."

He led Flurry away from the knot of men, though she looked as though she needed no calming down. She was sedate and confident in her gait. At a distance, he knelt beside her and pretended to be brushing her coat.

"Now tha sees how it is, Flurry," he said. "There's t'four pens at each corner. In each is a sheep. Tha has to go to each one, take t'sheep out, and then put all four into t'middle pen. . . . Now thee watch this one—this is t'Lancashire entry, and she was champion last year. And she's no slouch."

They watched the black sheep dog from Lancashire, sailing across the field at a gallop, neatly collecting the sheep.

"See how t'shepherd holds his crook like to make a door for t'middle pen, Flurry? Now that's all Ah can do to help. Ah can point or signal, but Ah can nobbut make a sort of angle to help wi' t'sheep at t'middle pen."

There was a burst of applause, which meant that the Lancashire dog had set the record time for the trial.

"Come on, then, Miss Smartie," Sam said. "It'll be us."

Sam heard his name being announced. He walked with Flurry to the ring. He knelt beside her.

"Now remember—no biting sheep or tha'll lose points."

She gave him a look that should have withered him.

"Go," said the judge.

Away Flurry sailed, her belly almost flat to the ground. She went from pen to pen, chivvying the sheep into a compact knot. She brought them to the center pen, driving at them adeptly so that before they could stand, sheep-wise and stubborn, and wonder where they were going, they were safe in the center pen. Then she sat at the gate, her tongue lolling out, and a burst of applause said she had made good time.

Sam hurried over to his mate. He rushed at Capper Wambley, who owned, without doubt, the finest watch in the village.

"How about it, Capper?"

The old man cleared his throat importantly and stared at his watch.

"Well. T'road Ah make it—wi' exact computations—is that there ain't a split-second difference between thee and Lancashire. But mind ye—that's unofficial, o' course."

So the chums rocked in impatience as the last tests were run off, and then they stood in the common hush as the judge took off his hat and advanced.

"First place," he announced, "is a tie between Joe Pettigill's Black Tad and Sam Small's Flurry, as far as time is concerned. But the judges unanimously award first place, on the basis o' calmer conduct in handling t'sheep, to Pettigill's Black Tad fro' Lancashire."

Of course, Sam and his friends were quite put out about it, and Gaffer Sitherthwick almost had apoplexy as he thought of his lost pound. . . . Thus it might have been a black day in the history of Polkingthorpe Brig had not Pettigill decided to gloat a bit. He walked over past the chums and said triumphantly, "Why don't ye all coom over to Lancashire and learn reight how to handle a tyke?"

This was, of course, too, too much for any Yorkshireman to bear. So Sam came right back at him. "Oh, aye?" he said.

It wasn't a very good answer, but it was all he could think of at the moment.

"Oh, aye," echoed Pettigill. . . .

"Ah admit tha's got a fine bitch there, Pettigill, but ma tyke ain't used to sheep. But if it came, now, to a test o' real intelligence—well, here's five pounds even fro' me and ma mates says we'll win at any contest tha says."

"Then thy good money goes after thy bad," the Lancashire lad said.

So it was arranged that an extra test would be held, with each man picking his own test to show the intelligence of his dog. Mr. Watcliffe, a well-to-do sheep dealer who was one of the judges, agreed to make the decision as to which dog was best.

The moor rang with excited chatter as the news spread, and everyone scurried around to lay bets. The Polkingthorpe men all got side bets down—except the Gaffer. He declined, morosely, to bet any more. So the contest got under way. Pettigill and Sam drew straws to see which dog should show off first.

Pettigill got the short straw and had to start. "Now, lass," he said to his dog, "over there Ah've put a stick, a stone, ma cap, and a handkerchief. Will some sporting gentleman call out which one Ah should bid her bring first?"

"T'stick!" a voice called.

"Tad. Fotch me yon stick," Pettigill ordered.

Away raced the dog and brought it. One by one, as requested, the champion brought back the correct articles, dropping them at its owner's feet. The men burst into applause as it ended. Then up stepped Sam. He knelt beside Flurry and spoke so all could hear.

"Lying i' front o' Joe Pettigill," he announced, "is four articles. When Ah say 'Go!' ma tyke'll first take t'cap, go to the far sheep pen, and drop it inside there. Next she'll take t'stick, and drop it at the feet o' t'biggest lad on this moor. Third she'll take t'stone and drop it at t'feet o' t'second-best dog trainer on this moor. Finally, she'll take t'handkerchief—" and here Sam beamed floridly—"and drop it afore t'handsomest and knowingest man around these parts. Now ista ready?"

Sam looked at Flurry, who jumped to her feet and leaned forward as if held by an invisible leash. The crowd almost moaned in a sort of excitement, for they had never heard of a dog that could understand such a complicated set of commands.

"Go!" said Sam.

Away sailed Flurry, veering past Joe Pettigill's feet and snatching up the cap on the dead gallop without stopping. Going in the water-smooth racing stride of a collie, she went out to the far pen, dropped the cap, and streaked back. She snatched the stick and loped toward the crowd. The men parted to let her through. She quested about, until she saw Ian Cawper. She dropped it at his feet and the men moaned astonishment.

Back she went for the stone. She picked it up, and then stood, as if at a loss. The men drew in their breath.

But Flurry merely looked up at Joe Pettigill, walked forward one step and dropped the stone again.

The men roared in approval.

"That means Pettigill's second-best dog trainer," they said. "But now for Sam!"

Flurry now had the handkerchief. She was walking to Sam, who stood, waiting triumphantly. Flurry came nearer to his feet, and then began to circle round him.

"She's forgot," the men breathed. "She don't know what to do wi' it."

Sam looked down, with a sort of agony in his eyes, for Flurry was trotting away from him—going away with the handkerchief in a hesitating sort of way. She was looking about her. She was walking to the center.

And then everyone saw what it was.

Flurry was going up to Mr. Watcliffe, the judge. She dropped the handkerchief at his feet, walked back to Sam, and sat properly at heel.

This time there was no cheering, for in that entire crowd it seemed as if a ghost had passed and lightly touched the back of every man's head, touching low down toward the neck where the short hairs grow, a touch that left a tingling sensation.

All one could hear was the voice of Mr. Watcliffe. "Why, bless my soul," he was saying. "Bless my very body and soul. She's almost human. Bless my soul."

Then he seemed to waken to his responsibility.

"Ah judge that the test has been won by Sam Small's tyke. If he will step forward, Ah'll give him the wager money."

This broke the spell. Sam went forward to collect, and the Polkingthorpe men went round with a roar to garner in the side bets they had made in the crowd. Everyone was in pocket except Gaffer Sitherthwick, which was also something to make that day a memorable one in Polkingthorpe's history. Seldom, if ever, did the Gaffer come out on the wrong side of money matters.

Together the chums all started home. Joe Pettigill stopped them and spoke like a true sport.

"That's a champion tyke tha has there, lad," he said.

"Thankee," said Sam with the customary modesty. "We nobbut won by luck."

"But how about ma cap up there?" the Lancashireman asked.

"Nay, Ah nobbut said she'd tak' it," Sam pointed out. "It'll cost thee another five pound to have her bring it back."

Pettigill frowned, then grinned in appreciation.

"Here, Tad," he said. "Go up and get ma cap." And away sailed his own fine dog.

Away, too, went Sam, with all the men slapping him on the back, applauding his wit, skill, acumen, and perspicacity. They streamed over the moor toward Polkingthorpe Brig to tell the story of their mighty triumph.

the hound and the hat

JAMES THURBER

wonder what a dog with a
fancy knit blanket on thinks about

CLARE BRIGGS

giving the trick dog the once over

T. A. DORGAN (TAD)

the deaf adder

COLIN HOWARD

Readers who remember Marcus, my huge, handsome, lazy, stupid St. Bernard, may be interested and incredulous to know that he recently had an idea.

Ideas are not things that come readily to St. Bernards. Their heads are not built for ideas. They bear a strong resemblance to that prehistoric monster that employed its head solely as a battering-ram, and kept its brains in its tail. Only of course a St. Bernard's tail is very little more intelligent than its head. This idea was certainly the first idea Marcus ever had in his life. I cannot think how he recognized it.

The idea had to do with the easing of life for St. Bernards. For some time past Marcus had been growing steadily more disgruntled with life. It is his belief that life should consist of sixteen hours of sleep, six hours of rest, and two hours of intensive eating. His only hobby is chasing cats, which he either loathes or considers edible—I am not sure which. However, the local cats do not suffer much. It will be seen that Marcus's day does not leave much time for cat-chasing.

But—and here lies the root of Marcus's moody dissatisfaction with life—he is occasionally called on to work. His work comprises a sullen amble after breakfast as far as the nearest corner and back. A real dog would look forward to this walk for hours beforehand, trembling with expectation. To Marcus it is sheer, brutal slavery.

Roughly, then, his idea was this: "If I were deaf I couldn't hear them when they called me for my walk, and they wouldn't be able to shift me, because nothing can shift me. So I will pretend to be deaf."

I do not claim Marcus thought it all out as neatly and briskly as that. He must have spent a good many weeks working out the advantages of deafness, and several more gloomily repining because he wasn't deaf. That he should pretend deafness was a flash of inspiration that probably seeped into his enormous head in a matter of days.

After all this thinking, Marcus presumably spent a month or two quietly recuperating under the kitchen table. The floor under the kitchen table is his favourite day-bed because he honestly believes he cannot be seen there, and therefore cannot be made to work. On the rare occasions that he rises, the table rises too. Highly-strung visitors, faced with this frightening apparition, have been known to go away and tell people we keep a howdah'd elephant in the kitchen.

At last he put his plan into execution. My wife came to me, much perturbed.

"Poor old Marcus has gone deaf!" she exclaimed.

"Deaf?" I cried. "But he could hear perfectly well last night."

"Well, he can't hear a thing now. Come and speak to him."

I came into the kitchen and addressed Marcus. Into his mournful eyes came the glazed expression of one who is jolly well not going to hear. I ought to have understood immediately; but who would credit a St. Bernard with having an idea?

"Poor old lad!" I said. "Perhaps it'll pass off. Coming for a walk, Marcus?"

Marcus, with masterly histrionism, gazed at me with eager devotion, as though he would have given his last bone to have heard what I said.

After a good deal of persuasive shouting we left him where he was, and he went to sleep smiling.

It was some days before we noticed Marcus was only partially deaf. He was still able to hear anything connected with food, such as a plate set on the floor to be licked, or a courteously-worded announcement that his supper was served. We went on talking to him about food and not talking to him about anything else. While this lasted he was the happiest St. Bernard in Great Britain. He wouldn't have changed with Rip van Winkle. But we realized a certain inconsistency about his deafness one Sunday when I was carving the joint. A tiny scrap of meat slipped from the fork and dropped onto the carpet. The dining-room is one room and a passage away from the kitchen, where Marcus, tired after his rest, was asleep, but he heard it fall. A blurred, tawny avalanche hurtled out of the kitchen and into the dining-room, and had wolfed the scrap almost before it had landed.

"Hey!" I said. "I thought you were deaf?"

Marcus's jaw and tail both dropped. He went back into character immediately, but the seeds of suspicion were sown. He lay down to rest—it is, as I have said, a long way from the kitchen to the dining-room—and to try to work out some logical means by which he could still hear anything to do with food but could remain deaf to all else.

He failed to find an answer, so he did without one. He continued to hear on one subject only. My wife, who is the most charitable person alive, and a constant film-goer, at first attributed this to schizophrenia. When we had finished arguing about the pronunciation, she went on to assert that this proved what she had always maintained—that Marcus had a mind somewhere. If he hadn't, she said, how could it be split? She wanted me to psychoanalyse him.

But even my wife grew suspicious of the selectivity of Marcus's hearing when, in one short hour, he failed to hear three commands to come out for a walk, one bellow to put that milk-

bottle down at once, a number of hysterical appeals to get out of her way for goodness' sake and let her get at the stove, and a stern lecture on the sanctity of the bread-board; but heard without difficulty a cat in the next road, the arrival of the butcher, and an invitation to finish a pot of fish-paste that had gone off.

When she was convinced of his guile she agreed with me he had to be cured. But how? The course we took was not, perhaps, entirely sporting. Marcus had gone deaf; *we* went silent.

When Marcus was around, we went through all the actions and expressions of speaking without uttering a word. Marcus began by being lazily puzzled. Very soon he was really worried. Had he overestimated his will-power and gone *really* deaf?

The horrible part of course was that, for all he knew, we might be talking food all day long, discussing dainties we had put out in the garden for Marcus, asking him if he fancied a few biscuits? The thought of what he might be missing was torture to him. He would lie staring agonizedly into our faces as we mouthed silently at one another—trying, I will swear, to lip-read.

As he never got called for meals, he had to look out for them himself, and he hardly dared close his eyes in case he missed one. I doubt if he got fourteen hours' real sleep out of the twenty-four, and he worried himself down to about three hun-dredweight.

We kept it up for a few days. Then we decided to restore Marcus's hearing to him. I said aloud: "Come on, Marcus! Time for your walk, boy!"

An expression of beautiful relief spread over his vast face, taking about one minute to do so. He wasn't deaf after all. He bounded to his feet. He frisked to the gate like a mettle-some carthorse. He joyously took one of the longest walks of his career—almost half a mile.

Heavens, how he slept that week!

He was not troubled again with his deafness. Neither were we.

Illustrated by Sprod

"Ready? One! Raise your arms above your head . . ."

TETSU

RONALD SEARLE

the coyote and the dog

from *Roughing It*

MARK TWAIN

Along about an hour after breakfast we saw the first prairie-dog villages, the first antelope, and the first wolf. If I remember rightly, this latter was the regular *coyote* (pronounced *ky-o-te*) of the farther deserts. And if it *was*, he was not a pretty creature, or respectable either, for I got well acquainted with his race afterward, and can speak with confidence.

The coyote is a long, slim, sick and sorry-looking skeleton, with a gray wolfskin stretched over it, a tolerably bushy tail that forever sags down with a despairing expression of forsakenness and misery, a furtive and evil eye, and a long, sharp face, with slightly lifted lip and exposed teeth. He has a general slinking expression all over. The coyote is a living, breathing allegory of Want. He is *always* hungry. He is always poor, out of luck and friendless. The meanest creatures despise him, and even the fleas would desert him for a velocipede. He is so spiritless and cowardly that even while his exposed teeth are pretending a threat, the rest of his face is apologizing for it. And he is *so* homely!—so scrawny, and ribby, and coarse-haired, and pitiful. When he sees you he lifts his lip and lets a flash of his teeth out, and then turns a little out of the course he was pursuing, depressing his head a bit, and strikes a long, soft-footed trot through the sagebrush, glancing over his shoulder at you, from time to time, till he is about out of easy pistol range, and then he stops and takes a deliberate survey of you; he will trot fifty yards and stop again—another fifty and stop again: and finally, the gray of his gliding body blends with the gray of the sagebrush, and he disappears.

All this is when you make no demonstration against him; but if you do, he develops a livelier interest in his journey, and instantly electrifies his heels and puts such a deal of real estate between himself and your weapon, that by the time you have raised the hammer you see that you need a Minié rifle, and by the time you have got him in line you need a rifled cannon, and by the time you have drawn a bead on him, you see well enough that nothing but an unusually long-winded streak of lightning could reach him where he is now. But if you start a swift-footed dog after him, you will enjoy it ever so much—especially if it is a dog that has a good opinion of himself, and has been brought up to think he knows something about speed. The coyote will go swinging gently off on that deceitful trot of his, and every little while he will smile a fraudful smile over his shoulder that will fill that dog entirely full of encouragement and worldly ambition, and make him lay his head still lower to the ground, and stretch his neck further to the front, and pant more fiercely, and stick his tail out straighter behind, and move his furious legs with a yet wilder frenzy, and leave a broader and broader, and higher and denser cloud of desert sand smoking behind, and marking his long wake across the level plain!

And all this time the dog is only a short twenty feet behind the coyote, and to save the soul of him he cannot understand why it is that he cannot get perceptibly closer, and he begins to get aggravated, and it makes him madder and madder to see how gently the coyote glides along and never pants or sweats or ceases to smile; and he grows still more and more incensed to see how shamefully he has been taken in by an entire stranger, and what an ignoble swindle that long, calm, soft-footed trot is; and next he notices that he is getting fagged, and that the coyote actually has to slacken speed a little to keep from running away from him—and *then* that town dog is mad in earnest, and he begins to strain and weep and swear, and paw the sand higher than ever, and reach for the coyote with concentrated and desperate energy. This spurt finds him six feet behind the gliding enemy, and two miles from his friends. And then, in the instant that a wild new hope is lighting up his face, the coyote turns and smiles blandly upon him once more, and with a something about it which seems to say: "Well, I shall have to tear myself away from you, but—business is business, and it will not do for me to be fooling along this way all day"—and forthwith there is a rushing sound, and the sudden splitting of a long crack through the atmosphere, and behold that dog is solitary and alone in the midst of a vast solitude!

It makes his head swim. He stops, and looks all around; climbs the nearest sand mound, and gazes into the distance; shakes his head reflectively, and then, without a word, he turns and jogs along back to his train, and takes up a humble position under the hindmost wagon, and feels unspeakably mean, and looks ashamed, and hangs his tail at half-mast for a week. And for as much as a year after that, whenever there is a great hue and cry after a coyote, that dog will merely glance in that direction without emotion, and apparently observe to himself, "I believe I do not wish any of the pie."

the slicker the vet,
the sicker the pet

from *The Rising Gorge*

S. J. PERELMAN

The demeanor of the veterinarian should be serious, though friendly; somewhat aloof, though with an air of sincerity; firm, though gentle and definite in his course of action. The client should be repeatedly reminded of every single thing that is being done for his pet until it sinks in. Charges should be clearly and distinctly specified; and because neurotics are unpredictable, total payment or at least a substantial payment should be made in advance. The payment will have a further salutary effect in instilling the client with the confidence that not only is everything possible being done, but in paying for it he feels that he has done the best for his pet's benefit.

Some neurotic clients will often abuse the telephone service. It is therefore both disarming and pleasing to the client to be telephoned by the veterinarian. This is dramatically satisfying especially if the news is good. When the news is not good, the veterinarian should express deep personal concern—as if the possible loss of the pet is as poignant to him as to the owner.—*From "The Neurotic Pet Owner," a paper by A. Barton, D.V.M., reprinted in* Philadelphia Medicine.

The blacktop road out of Churl's Point, where they confirmed my directions, was fringed by stock farms, great barbered estates full of pedigreed Angus and Guernseys eating their heads off on the rolling clover slopes. A warm glow enveloped me as I thought of their harassed owners, advertising men toiling away over media and research in some Manhattan honeycomb to meet the feed bills. It would have been sweet to pause and gloat over their predicament, but Buddy, tethered in the rear of the station wagon, was yelping so dolorously that I decided to press on. Less than a mile beyond, I came abreast of a squat oblong of redwood with a row of exercise pens in back which answered the description of the vet's establishment. The glass-brick portico sheltered a geometrical pair of ilexes and a sign reading, "Burning Bush Animal Hospital—Walk In."

"Well, here we are, good boy," I said, with forced heartiness, untying Buddy's leash. He sniffed suspiciously, then flattened his ears and bared his fangs in a half snarl. "Come on, now," I urged, tugging him down. "Nobody's going to hurt you. Be nice." He wanted to be nothing of the sort, and, for an under-sized Shetland sheepdog, managed to simulate twice his weight as I dragged him inside. The only occupant of the claustropho-bic anteroom was a hard-featured blonde in slacks, holding a Pekinese. Selecting the chair opposite, I sank into contempla-tion of the knotty-pine wall, graced with a flyblown diploma and Senator Vest's tribute to his dog, behind her head. Within a few seconds, Buddy finished his inspection of the area around us and started edging toward our neighbor.

"Pardon me, Miss," I said as she leaned forward to pat him. "I'd be careful, if those slacks you're wearing are flannel."

She withdrew her hand, eying me with hauteur. "What's that got to do with it?"

"I was only trying to warn you—"

"I don't see it's any of your business what my slacks are made of," she said, her nostrils distending dangerously.

"Please don't misunderstand," I apologized. "I'll tell you why I brought it up."

"Tell your diary," she snapped, and arose. "I've heard that ploy before, Mister, and it creaks. Lucky for you my husband's in the Navy."

Lucky for my aplomb as well, a door at the rear simultaneously flew open and Dr. Myron Vulpein emerged. His smock
and his sallow, concave face, bisected by a hairline mustache,
gave him the rather anomalous look of a barber, but a duly por-
tentous frown betokened the medical man. With a crisp injunc-
tion to follow the treatment he had outlined within, he extended
a phial to the blonde. She was to further remember, he continued sternly, that every scientific resource was being ex-
pended on her pet, all the knowledge gleaned from decades of
painstaking research. "Do you understand that? Has that sunk
in?" he demanded. "O.K., then, forget about your pooch. He's
in the lap of the gods—your conscience is clear. . . . This
way, sir."

With a grimace indicative of her deep distaste for me, the
lady swept out, and Buddy and I straggled into the consult-
ing room. After a grueling interrogation on why I had sought
him out, as though I were a junkie, Vulpein bade me relate
my story. I explained that my wife and I were boarding the
animal temporarily for his master, an actor friend currently
on tour, and that his deportment had been unexceptionable
up to the previous weekend. Then, for no apparent reason,
he had begun to evince a disturbing penchant for the nether
garments of our guests, furtively gnawing and perforating their
trouser legs under the dinner table.

"Let me get that straight," said Vulpein. A faintly sardonic
smile revealed that he had already classified me psychologically.
"Did—er—anyone else besides you notice this phenomenon?"

"What do you mean?" I said, bristling. "The people whose
clothes he ate, my wife— You couldn't *help* but notice. Their
pants were full of holes."

"Of course, of course," he said soothingly. "And was that the
only occasion on which he molested your friends?"

"No, the same thing happened the next night, with a whole
different group," I said. "The worst of it is, you're not con-

scious of what he's doing. He just nibbles at the cloth, soft little bites, like fish stealing bait off a hook."

"I see," said Vulpein, joining his fingertips in Baker Street fashion. "Now, were there any other factors you consider pertinent or relevant?"

"Well—" I hesitated. "Maybe it was coincidence, but he seemed to concentrate mainly on woolen slacks and flannels. He didn't bother the people who were wearing cabardines or gorduroy."

His eyes, narrowed in absorption, opened to betray a sudden gleam. "Mmm, highly significant," he said. "For your information. it's *gaba*rdines, and *cor*duroy. Excuse me a moment—I must call one of my clients." He dialed a number, and as a reedy voice echoed from the receiver, assumed a rabbinical, almost seraphic expression. "Mrs. Horniman?" he inquired. "Dr. Vulpein. I have very encouraging news for you about your parakeet. He took a little spin on his Ferris wheel this morning after breakfast. . . . Well, I wouldn't be too optimistic, but I think we're over the hump. . . . You're welcome. Goodbye." When he turned back to me, however, all geniality had flown. "From the symptoms you describe," he announced, "I'd say the animal was suffering from a serious nutritional deficiency. In layman's terms, he's not getting some vital ingredient."

"I never knew dogs needed wool in their diet," I said puzzled. "We feed him round ground, table scraps—"

"It might be one of a hundred things," he broke in. "Some obscure oil or vitamin in the cloth that he seeks out instinctively —we won't know till I analyze the material. I presume you brought along a swatch for that purpose?"

"How could I?" I objected. "I can't very well ask my friends to hack up their trousers. I mean, they're pretty browned off as it is."

"Well, it's not really essential," said Vulpein. "In any case, we'll have to keep him under observation here a few days to watch his behavior. That'll be sixty dollars—in advance." I opened my mouth to protest, but he quickly forestalled me. However excessive I deemed the fee, it was puny; the heartsease it purchased, the assurance that I was doing my utmost for Buddy, was incomputable. At last, in view of my limited responsibility to the beast, he grudgingly agreed to accept half the amount, and with a caveat to refrain from introspection and unnecessary phone calls, dismissed me. "He'll be on his feet in no time," he declared (a somewhat loose interpretation of the problem, I felt) . "I'll ring you as soon as we have any developments to report, if not sooner."

He was as good as his word; three days later, I received a bulletin that Buddy had been allowed free access to Vulpein's table at mealtime but had caused no visible depredations. Knowing the dog's sly nature, I hazarded the opinion that he was aware he was being watched. "He's too foxy to tip his mitt to a stranger," I insisted. "Couldn't you lock him up in your bedroom, say, with an old pair of flannels?"

"Force his hand, eh?" mused Vulpein. "By jingo, I'll do better than that! You know those dummies they have in haberdashery stores? I think I'll borrow one from Guzik's, in Allentown, and duplicate the exact conditions under which he ate the material."

Whether he meant to reconstruct our dining room in its entirety—a job that would have necessitated more cobwebs than he possessed—he failed to specify, but, on deliberation, I detected a flaw in his scheme. Whatever Buddy's shortcomings, he was much too crafty to be deluded by a wax mannequin mutely posed at a table; some form of sound or dialogue was obligatory to give the scene the illusion of reality. Unluckily, the only record I had on hand at the moment was a poetry reading of Mr. Eliot's, and the thought of Buddy nuzzling the dummy to the lugubrious cadences of "The Waste Land" was inadmissible. Extensive search of the attic, though, yielded up a fair copy of "Cohen on the Telephone," which I forthwith sent along, with a chit outlining how it was to be used. When,

after a lapse of several days with no contact between us, I
phoned Vulpein, there was a distinct note of wariness in his
manner.

"How are you feeling?" he asked.

"Tiptop," I said, taken aback a bit. "Why shouldn't I?"

"Oh, nothing," he replied casually. "You—er—you haven't
heard any unusual noises, or voices in your head?"

"Look here," I barked. "What the deuce are you implying?
I call up to inquire about a dog—"

"Now, don't get hot under the collar," he placated me. "In
my profession these days, we strive for the over-all picture. If
your emotional barometer's stormy, your pet may be wacky,
too." Such was far from the case with Buddy, he hastened to
add; despite prolonged exposure to the dummy and three
changes of trouser, the animal had not ravaged a single thread.
"Probably just a passing aberration," concluded Vulpein, "but
I'd advise making one last check to set your mind at rest. Invite
some person to dinner that he originally pestered, if possible
wearing the exact same clothes. I'll bring the dog over during
the meal so we can study his reactions together."

The project, as I foresaw at once, was going to be no choco-
late soda; solicited to break bread again with us, most of Buddy's
victims refused point-blank. Finally, Joyce and Waldo Muscatine, a couple enslaved by six poodles and hence past-experts
on canine behavior, consented to attend, but I decided it would
be crowding my luck to designate their attire, and I was relieved
when Waldo showed up in suntans. The cocktail interlude and
soup passed off uneventfully, except that I caught Waldo stealing repeated glances under the table.

"Where's that crummy sheepdog you had around here?" he
queried at length.

"The Shetland pup?" I said lightly. "Oh, he's over at the
vet's having a checkup—at Dr. Vulpein's."

"Vulpein?" Joyce repeated. *"Myron* Vulpein?" I nodded, and

her eyes protruded in horror. "That—that monster!" she exploded. "I took one of our dogs to him for a simple flea bath, and he told me I was a masochist!"

"Well, he's right," asserted her husband. "Anybody who has six dogs—"

"I don't care!" she declaimed. "He's a nasty, insulting creep, and if I ever meet him again, I'll tell him so!"

"Joyce, there's something you ought to know," I began, but the doorbell cut me short. I skillfully avoided looking at my wife, having seen a stone wife before, and went to answer it. Dr. Vulpein in mufti seemed even less the healer than he had during our colloquy; in his raglan topcoat and sporty porkpie, he could have been an insurance adjuster or a tout. "Er—come in, won't you, Doctor?" I said, and peered around him. "Where's the dog?"

He blinked at me, obviously reluctant to answer. "I'm afraid I'm the bearer of bad tidings," he said, advancing into the room. "He's vanished—disappeared into thin air." His voice took on a tremulous, grief-stricken quality. "I can't account for it," he said hoarsely. "We'd just left the turnpike at Cross Keys when he suddenly leaped from the car and ran into the fields. I searched and searched—"

"Well, that doesn't surprise *me!*" I heard Joyce announce triumphantly behind me. "He's got more sense than some people I've met!"

As Vulpein, perplexed, wheeled to confront her, I uttered a sound intended as a conciliatory chuckle. "Excuse me," I said. "I believe you know each other. Mrs. Muscatine, Dr. Vulpein." "Oh, yes indeedy I know him," Joyce grated. "He's the kid who's assumed the mantle of Sigmund Freud. Haven't you, Doctor?"

Vulpein subjected her to a Himalayan stare. "I'm merely a licensed veterinarian, Madam," he rejoined glacially, "but I can recognize a hysteroid when I meet one."

"Hey, wait a minute, you!" Waldo called out, springing up. "What did you call my wife?"

Well, that was it in a nutshell, so to speak. The next thing I knew, the air was full of curt words and women's shrieks, and two gladiators were slugging it out, toe to toe, on the Axminster. Waldo got a swollen nose for his gallantry, and Vulpein got a summons the next day for assault, which I doubt will stand up in court. I fully expect to do so, though, when our actor friend returns from the road. He'll never believe my explanations about Buddy. He's an absolute neurotic on the subject of pets.

why mothers get gray

J. R. WILLIAMS

J. W. TAYLOR

THELWELL

SPROD

"We're hoping that one day he'll remember his errand
and go off as mysteriously as he came."

SIGGS

dogs and public service

from *From Bed to Worse*

ROBERT BENCHLEY

The meter-readers and collectors for the Consolidated Gas Company of New York City do not seem to have quite caught the knack of making friends with dogs. During the past year 198 of them were badly enough bitten to require medical attention. This sort of thing obviously couldn't go on, even from the dogs' point of view.

So the company has issued a book of instructions to its 20,000 employes. It is called "Dogs: How to Approach and Handle Them," and, according to *Time,* it contains the following rules:

1. Make a little noise, to let the dog know that you are coming.
2. Show no alarm at growls or barks. They are simply challenges.
3. Welcome the dog's acquaintance-making sniffs.
4. Make no sudden or unnatural movements.
5. Speak only in a confident, friendly voice.
6. Keep your hands off.
7. Impress the dog with the propriety of your visit.

These rules sound simple, but I should think that one or two of them would call for quite a bit of finesse. The last one, Rule No. 7, for example. How would you go about impressing a dog with the propriety of your visit?

My instinct would be to say to the dog, "in a confident, friendly voice" (Rule No. 5): "Come on over here on the steps a minute, old boy. I want to talk to you." Then, when you and he were comfortably seated, you could point out to him that every age and every country has had varying standards of what is proper and what isn't proper.

"Propriety is a question of environment," you could tell him, "and it is only a very narrow-minded person who tries to impose his standards of propriety on others. And you don't want to be thought narrow-minded, do you, Werewolf?"

And he would probably shake his head, possibly with his teeth still in the calf of your leg.

Then you could show him that, under our present economic system (which is already undergoing radical changes) it is necessary for public service corporations to make collections and make repairs, and that, so long as we live under this system (a bad one, you agree), people like you must, of necessity, make periodic calls.

"You see that, don't you, old fellow?" you could ask, just before you faint. And, if he is any kind of dog at all he will be impressed with the propriety of your visit and let go.

Just what "little noise" could be made to let the dog know that you are coming (Rule No. 1) is another problem. You might begin skipping and singing, "I'm coming, I'm coming!"

just as you get to the gate, or perhaps carry a zither with you and strum a few chords softly in the middle distance. Another good way would be to hide behind the gatepost and call out: "Guess who's here! Gassy-mansy!" and then appear slowly, waggling a finger coyly.

On second thought, perhaps that wouldn't be so good. It might come under the head of "unnatural movements," which are warned against in Rule No. 4. The business of welcoming the dog's "acquaintance-making sniffs" and speaking in "a confident, friendly voice" is all very well, and goes hand in hand with "showing no alarm at growls or barks." These are the tactics that I invariably adopt, but I sometimes wonder if they fool the dog. My cheery "How are ya, boy?" spoken much too loudly and with a great deal too much confidence, has often failed to impress even me, especially if the dog keeps on growling.

Dogs are no fools, and I have a feeling that they recognize the sham and have contempt for it. I think that it might be better just to shut your eyes and walk right by, without any "How are ya, boy?" at all. Then at least, you would be keeping your self-respect, if not the cuff to your trouser leg.

It is a difficult problem that the Gas Company faces, and an even more difficult one that its employes face. Why couldn't householders just be taught to make their own repairs, and have the company let the unpaid bills ride?

Illustrated by Gluyas Williams

the dog

OGDEN NASH

The truth I do not stretch or shove
When I state the dog is full of love.
I've also proved, by actual test,
A wet dog is the lovingest.

on buying a dog

EDGAR KLAUBER

"I wish to buy a dog," she said,
"A dog you're sure is quite well bred,
In fact, I'd like some guarantee
He's favored with a pedigree."

"My charming friend," the pet man said,
"I have a dog that's so well bred,
If he could talk, I'll guarantee
He'd never speak to you or me."

butch and the lark

from *The World, the Flesh, and H. Allen Smith*

H. ALLEN SMITH

Whenever possible the Blairs take Butch with them on out-of-town trips. Once they went to San Francisco, engaging a bedroom on The Lark, a train which is customarily greeted in the Los Angeles station by shouts from railroad workers who cry, "Hark! Hark! The Lark!"

The Blairs got Butch into the bedroom without difficulty but from then on there were unpleasant developments. Butch has a habit of exposing his fangs and snarling, presenting a prospect that would frighten the late Albert Payson Terhune. Moreover, Butch is suspicious of anybody in a uniform. The conductor who came for the tickets was the first victim of this suspicion, and the transaction finally had to be consummated under the door. White-jacketed waiters all but got their heads torn off whenever they tried to bring Mr. Blair's bourbon, and they ended up by refusing to serve him. During the night Butch spent all his time trying to climb into the upper berth where his master was losing sleep. The dog barked and howled and screamed, and the other passengers pounded on the walls, and complained bitterly to the train officials.

At last they reached San Francisco. Mr. Blair got Butch off the train and started down the platform. He encountered the conductor and, with the intention of placating that gentleman, said:

"Butch didn't behave himself very well on the trip, did he?

I hope he doesn't act up like that on the return trip."

"Are you taking him back to L. A.?" asked the conductor.

"My wife is," said Mr. Blair. "Going back next week—on The Lark."

"Oh no, he's not," said the conductor. "That dog is never going anywhere again on The Lark. That dog made this run a hell on earth and I intend to say as much in my report. You'll not get him on The Lark, or on any other trains belonging to this company."

"We'll see," said Mr. Blair abruptly. He is a man who loves nothing more than to find an obstacle that needs surmounting.

Yet the conductor's mandate gave him some worry. He planned to remain in San Francisco awhile and Mrs. Blair was to return with Butch. Mr. Blair was determined that Butch should ride The Lark back to Hollywood.

He went out and bought a pair of dark glasses. Then he bought a Seeing Eye dog harness.

He took Mrs. Blair and Butch to the station. Mrs. Blair had on the dark glasses and Butch, wearing the harness, was supposed to be impersonating a Seeing Eye dog. He did all right until they got through the ticket gate. The moment he saw the train he went into rebellion. He wanted nothing whatever to do with that iron monster. He started growling, flopped down on his belly, and refused to move another inch.

By good fortune another conductor was in charge of the train, else the plot would have died right then. In any event, passengers and trainmen were treated to a unique spectacle.

Down the platform came a blind woman, dragging her Seeing Eye dog along the concrete. Over the stubborn dog stood a man, cursing the animal fluently. The blind woman dragged that dog all the way down the platform and then the man spent ten minutes wrestling with the animal, boosting him into the vestibule of the car.

In spite of Butch's rebellious performance, they got away with it.

mr. gerolman loses his dog

from *The Rise and Fall of the Mustache*

ROBERT J. BURDETTE

Mr. Gerolman stood on the front porch of his comfortable home on West Hill one morning looking out at the drizzling rain in anything but a comfortable frame of mind. He looked up and down the yard, and then he raised his umbrella and went to the gate and looked up and down the street. Then he whistled in a very shrill manner three or four times, and listened as though he was expecting a response. If he was, he was disappointed, for there was no response save the pattering of the rain on his umbrella, and he frowned heavily as he returned to the porch, from which sheltered post of observation he gloomily surveyed the dispiriting weather.

"Dag gone the dag gone brute," he muttered savagely, "if ever I keep another dog again, I hope it will eat me up."

And then he whistled again. And again there was no response. It was evident that Mr. Gerolman had lost his dog, a beautiful ashes of roses hound with seal brown spots and soft satin-finish ears. He was a valuable dog, and this was the third time he had been lost, and Mr. Gerolman was rapidly losing his temper as completely as he had lost his dog. He lifted his voice and called aloud:

"H'yuh - h - h Ponto! h'yuh Ponto! h'yuhp onto! h'yup onto, h'yup onto, h'yuponto, h'yuponto! h'yup, h'yup, h'yup!"

185

As he ceased calling, and looked anxiously about for some indications of a dog, the front door opened and a woman's face, shaded with a tinge of womanly anxiety and fastened to Mrs. Gerolman's head, looked out.

"The children call him Hector," a low sweet voice said for the wistful, pretty face; but the bereaved master of the absent dog was in no humor to be charmed by a beautiful face and a flute-like voice.

"By George," he said, striding out into the rain and purposely leaving his umbrella on the porch to make his wife feel bad, "it's no wonder the dog gets lost, when he has so dod binged many names that he don't know himself. By Jacks, when I give eleven dollars for a dog, I want the privilege of naming him, and the next person about this house that tries to fasten an old pagan, Indian, blasphemous name on a dog of mine, will hear from me about it; now that's all."

And then he inflated his lungs and yelled like a scalp hunter.

"Here, Hector! here, Hector! here rector, hyur, rector, hyur rec, h'yurrec, k'yurrec k'yurrec, k'yurrec! Godfrey's cordial, where's that dog gone to? H'yuponto, h'yupont! h'yuh, h'yuh, h'yuh! I hope he's poisoned—h'yurrector! By George, I do; h'yuh Ponto, good dog, Ponty, Ponty, Ponty, h'yuh Pont! I'd give fifty dollars if some one had strychnined the nasty, worthless, lop-eared cur; hyurrec, k'yurrec! By granny, I'll kill him when he comes home, if I don't I hope to die; h'yuh Ponto, h'yuh Ponto, *h'yuh* Hec!!"

And as he turned back to the porch the door again opened and the tremulous voice sweetly asked:

"Can't you find him?"

"Naw!!!" roared the exasperated dog-hunter, and the door closed precipitately and was opened no more during the session.

"Here, Ponto!" roared Mr. Gerolman, from his position on the porch, "Here, Hector!" And then he whistled until his head swam and his throat was so dry you could light a match in it. "Here, Ponto! Blast the dog. I suppose he's twenty-five

miles from here. Hector! What are you lookin' at, you gimlet-
eyed old Bedlamite?" he savagely growled, apostrophizing a
sweet-faced old lady with silky white hair, who had just looked
out of her window to see where the fire was, or who was being
murdered. "Here, Ponto! here Ponto! Good doggie, nice old
Pontie, nice old Heckie dog—Oh-h-h," he snarled, dancing up
and down on the porch in an ecstasy of rage and impatience,
"I'd like to tramp the ribs out of the long-legged worthless old
garbage eater; *here, Ponto, here!*"

To his amazement he heard a canine yawn, a longdrawn,
weary kind of a whine, as of a dog who was bored to death
with the dismal weather; then there was a scraping sound, and
the dog, creeping out from under the porch, from under his
very feet, looked vacantly around as though he wasn't quite
sure but what he had heard some one calling him, and then
catching sight of his master, sat down and thumped on the
ground with his tail, smiled pleasantly, and asked as plainly
as ever dog asked in the world,

"Were you wanting me?"

Mr. Gerolman, for one brief instant, gasped for breath. Then
he pulled his hat down tight on his head, snatched up his umbrella with a convulsive grasp and yelled "Come 'ere!" in such
a terrific roar that the white-haired old lady across the way fell
back in a fit, and the dog, surmising that all was not well, briefly
remarked that he had an engagement to meet somebody about
fifty-eight feet under the house, and shot under the porch like
a shooting dog-star. Mr. Gerolman made a dash to intercept
him, but stumbled over a flower stand and plunged through
a honey-suckle trellis, off the porch, and down into a raging
volcano of moss-rose bush, straw, black dirt, shattered umbrella
ribs, and a ubiquitous hat, while far under the house, deep in
the cavernous darkness, came the mocking laugh of an ashes of
roses dog with seal brown spots, accompanied by the taunting
remark as nearly as Mr. Gerolman could understand the dog,

"Who hit him? Which way did he go?"

fifteen ways to clip a poodle

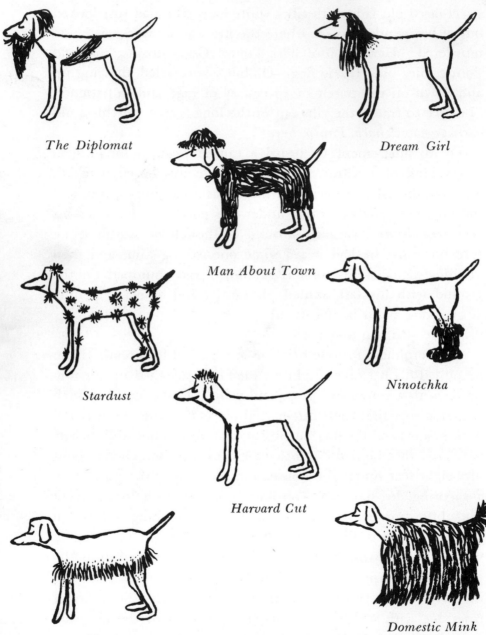

The Diplomat

Dream Girl

Man About Town

Stardust

Ninotchka

Harvard Cut

Flapper

Domestic Mink

Lorelei

Purity

Fireworks

Mystery Man

Glamour

Song of the Islands

Hot Rod

ROY McKIE

sunning

JAMES S. TIPPETT

Old Dog lay in the summer sun
Much too lazy to rise and run.
He flapped an ear
At a buzzing fly.
He winked a half open
Sleepy eye,
He scratched himself
On an itching spot,
As he dozed on the porch
Where the sun was hot.
He whimpered a bit
From force of habit
While he lazily dreamed
Of chasing a rabbit.
But Old Dog happily lay in the sun
Much too lazy to rise and run.

graham's dogs

"*There—she's started!*"

"*I've been worried sick . . .*"

"Settle down!"

"He hates having his claws clipped . . ."

"How was he to know it was meant for your supper?"

"An alert, intelligent dog would have given the alarm."

mad dogs
and englishmen

from *The Day of the Dog*

MICHAEL FRAYN

I don't usually ask for charity, but if anyone could spare a little
for the Distressed Gentledogs Aid Association, I know a hundred tails that would wag a little faster tonight. Ordinary dogs
have the Canine Defence League, but what of the dog who is
set apart from his fellows by having within him something
higher, something nobler?

Take, for instance, case No. 472/G/9 on the association's files.
I quote it as it appeared in all its heartbreaking detail in the
columns of *The Grocer:*

> An unusual sales promotion for Ful-o-Pep dog food will take place
> in the Bristol area next week. A man, dressed as a dog, will be
> parading the main shopping centres and will be offering to return
> to the housewife the purchase price of any packet of Ful-o-Pep
> she has in her basket or has bought recently provided she can pro-
> duce the packet top. Every hundredth customer who approaches
> the "dog" will be asked a general knowledge question and if it
> is answered correctly will be given free a transistor radio set.

Urgent arrangements are being made to offer assistance in
this case on the assumption that it will turn out in much the
same sort of way as case No. 359/F/2. In this, a man dressed
as a dog was sent out to publicise Bags-o-Gudness dog food in

the Totnes area by very similar means. After a short while, however, he was taken into custody by the police, and his employer, Mr. Bags O'Gudness, was charged with failing to keep his dog under proper control, and with keeping a dog without a licence.

Several women appeared in court to give evidence that they had been terrified when the huge dog had bounded up to them in the street and snuffled about among the contents of their shopping baskets. One woman said the dog had pulled out a packet of dog food she was taking home for her Scottie, another that the dog had chased her up a cul-de-sac, cornered her with bared teeth and snarled: "What was the date of George IV's accession to the throne?"

Mr. O'Gudness said that the dog—which was called Edward Arthur Brown, and was aged forty-nine—was not exactly a dog in the normal sense of the word. "I have always regarded Brown more as a friend than a dog," he said, "and I was afraid he would take offense if I tried to licence him, or put him on a chain." A police constable told the court that when he had taken the dog to the station and charged it, it had replied: "Help. Get me out of this. The zip is stuck."

The magistrate gave O'Gudness an absolute discharge. The Court, he said, sympathised with him in his attempts to behave equitably towards Brown. Brown was clearly a dog of unusual accomplishments—but that did not mean he could be allowed to pursue his eccentric behaviour unchecked. He ordered that Brown should be placed in the psychiatric centre run by the Distressed Gentledogs Aid Association for treatment.

When Brown arrived at the centre it was clear he was a very sick dog indeed. His adjustment to his environment was profoundly disturbed—he exhibited hysteria when introduced into a cage full of other dogs under treatment, threw the plateful of Bags-o-Gudness he was given at the waiter, and tried to bite his analyst.

The analyst diagnosed an acute anxiety state, which took

the form of struggling with pathetic desperation to open an imaginary zip fastener. Underneath his exterior, which appeared as normal as the next dog's, there seemed to be a totally different personality, morbid and self-pitying. Brown, it became clear, lived in a fantasy world, absolutely convinced that he was married to a woman called Deidre, and would one day return to her and their two children in a semi-detached house at Dawlish.

The road to recovery is of course slow. After prolonged sedation, Brown is being persuaded to eat, sleep, and exercise with other dogs without alarm, and is being taught simple tricks, like dying for his country and begging for his Bags-o-Gudness. In a year or two he will be allowed out for walks—on the lead, of course. By that time, thanks to our devoted care, he may even be well enough to say "thank you" to the Distressed Gentledogs Aid Association—not in the verbal language of his old fantasy world, but, like any other normal dog, by simply barking, wagging his tail, and licking his analyst's hand.

living with a dog

ROGER ANGELL

There is a sports columnist for a New York newspaper who, on days when a double-header has been rained out or when Madison Square Garden is taken up with the antique show, likes to take a kick at dogs in his column. This fellow doesn't like dogs, and he says so. He doesn't understand dogs, has never lived with a dog, and wants no part of a dog. All this is perfectly O.K. with me; if he can't take dogs, he is at liberty to leave them alone and say so, and besides, six full columns a week is a lot of space for any man to fill with nothing but interviews with prize fighters and jockeys.

My beef with this sportswriter is over what he has to say about dog *owners*. It is his firm belief that a man who keeps a dog is first cousin to a heroin addict. A pet dog, he says, is nothing more than a shot in the arm to a man's ego—occasional evidence that he is a truly superior being. In keeping a dog around the house a man is merely making sure that there is at least one creature who will always love him, no matter what. He points out that a dog owner can drink up the rent money, snarl at his kids, beat his wife, and lie around in bed all day with a scratch sheet and still have the undying affection of his dog. The reason for this, he says, is simple: a dog is a singularly unprincipled and lazy animal who long ago discovered that a

197

wag of the tail and a misty look in his eyes for his master would save him the trouble of going out and working for a square meal. A dog's loyalty is always reserved for the latest person to put down a dish of Red Heart for him.

All this, of course, is pure fantasy, as anybody knows who has ever had a dog around the house long enough to be on speaking terms with him. I know, because I am a dog owner of long standing and I have the scars—on my body, my furniture and my psyche—to prove it. I am prepared to explain to this dogless columnist exactly what living with a dog entails. I am rendering him this service entirely gratis, out of a simple desire to win more sympathy for dog owners, who, God knows, are in acute need of it.

First of all, let me confess that I am a patsy for a dog. I must be, or I wouldn't put up with the punishment. At the moment, the dog in my life is a muscular, rather numskulled English bulldog named Levi. He has been living with us for a year and a half now and I have just figured out, with pencil and paper, that the amount of my time I have given, almost entirely unwillingly, to attending Levi's odd needs and excessive demands, would have enabled me to write a long historical novel, log fifteen strokes off my golf score, or become an expert on French brandies. In those eighteen months, for instance, I have four times (twice by pond, twice by sea) rescued our dog from drowning, simply because he is laboring under the insane delusion that he is a canine Weissmuller. I am not counting here the number of times I have fished him out of small streams and lakes he happened to tumble into merely because he was thinking of something else when he came across them. I once pulled him out of an open elevator shaft he had overlooked. I have pushed Levi about ten miles in my daughter's perambulator, simply because she once insisted that he join her on the seat and I, like a fool, thought it might be funny. Now both of them insist on it.

Consider, if you will, the absurd amount of inconvenience, wasted energy, and confusion involved in the mere act of taking Levi out of our apartment for a necessary breath of air. The signal for this is always relayed by my wife, who announces, "I think he wants to go out." Since this usually happens just as I am on the last chapter of the book I am reading or at the crux of an insanely funny story I am telling our guests, I am instantly upset and on the defensive. The dog, of course, has given no signal; he is either sleeping or thinking about swimming. "How do you know?" I ask my wife.

"Well," she says, "He just looks that way. You know, worried."

If my daughter is around, she insists on accompanying me on this brief excursion. In wintertime, this results in a long struggle with snowsuit and zippers, a search for mittens, firm rejection of the suggestion that we also take along a tricycle and a couple of toys, and, not infrequently, tears. Even if the dog and I manage to get out of the apartment alone, we are apt to encounter trouble in the elevator, in the form of two elderly ladies, one of whom lives on the eighth floor, the other on the eleventh. Eighth Floor is convinced that my dog is the most vicious public enemy since Alvin Karpis. When she encounters him in the elevator, she flattens herself against the wall and murmurs, "Nice doggy," in an effort to save herself from instant dismemberment. The dog, of course, thinks she is the nicest lady he has ever laid eyes on and always tries to put his paws up on her stomach so that she can scratch his ears. Eleventh Floor, on the other hand, is just mad for Levi; the moment she meets him, she gets right down on all fours on the elevator floor and starts to talk baby talk to him—a habit which both Levi and I find hideously embarrassing.

This foolish state of affairs is not unusual; any dog owner (any city dog owner, at least) could offer a matching recital. The point is simple: a dog's capacity to inflate the ego of his

owner is almost nil. His capacity to irk him, inconvenience
him, put him at odds with his family and himself, and generally
embarrass and belittle him is almost unbounded.

Take the case of Chloe and the Chicago railroad station.
Chloe was a Saint Bernard we had during the war. I was stationed at an army post in Denver at the time, where my wife
and I and Chloe lived in a small one-story house. When I was
ordered to ship out overseas, I received the usual fifteen-day
furlough, and Chloe joined us on the train trip to New York.
When our streamliner arrived in Chicago, I hurried up and
retrieved Chloe from the baggage car, where she had spent
a comfortable night. The three of us set off through the
crowded Chicago Northwestern Terminal, following our porters
toward the taxi which was to take us to our next train. Holding
Chloe's leash, I had just started down the long, double flight
of stairs which leads from the station's platform, when I was
brought up short with a tremendous jerk. Looking back, I saw
our dog, all four tremendous feet planted, looking down the
flight of stairs with an expression of stark horror. "C'mon,
Chloe," I said impatiently, twitching on the leash. But Chloe
wasn't having any of *that*. This time I tugged; Chloe tugged
back and I landed on my knees on the steps. I called my wife
back for consultation. "It's perfectly simple," she said. "She's
never seen a flight of stairs before."

"But that's stupid," I said. "She's a grown dog now—full
grown. Besides, they're supposed to be Alpine dogs."

"Well, you'll just have to carry her," my wife said. "I'll meet
you at the cab platform."

Chloe was only about a year old then, but she had her
growth—and then some. I imagine she must have gone a good
hundred and ten pounds. I unbuttoned my overcoat, collared
the animal (who was trying to hide under a newsstand), and
somehow heaved her into my arms and started a staggering
journey down the stairs. I had taken about three steps down

when Chloe let out a scream. It was no whimper, but a scream
—a terrified, feminine, high-pitched yodel. I imagine every
person in the station heard it. I couldn't see much with a Saint
Bernard in my arms, but everyone I *could* see had stopped
cold in his tracks and was staring at me. I continued downward
and Chloe continued screaming at every step. By the time I
reached the bottom, there were two M.P.'s with brassards and
clubs waiting for me.

"Watcha doin' to that dog?" the sergeant said angrily.

I put Chloe down and straightened up with difficulty. "I
was carrying her," I said.

"Oh, yeah? She don't look crippled to me. What was all that
yellin' and hooraw for?"

"Yeah," said the other M.P. darkly. "I *like* dogs."

"She's scared of stairs," I said wearily. "She's never seen
stairs before."

"Unh-huh," the sergeant said. "Let's see your dog tags,
soldier."

I had to show my dog tags, my furlough papers, and then
summon my wife over to back me up before I could get out
of that station. It didn't seem likely at the time that Chloe
would figure out another way to embarrass me but the following morning, when we arrived in the main concourse of Grand
Central Terminal, she did. It was a less original way, but
just as embarrassing.

It's not that I blame Chloe in the least. She was innocent
in the whole affair, just as most dogs are more or less innocent
when they get their owners into the most fantastic kind of
trouble. After a while your well-broken dog owner just gets
to expect that sort of thing. Just the other day I was telling
a man about Chloe and those stairs and he came up with a
similar Army dog experience. Worse, if anything.

Seems that this man had been stationed at a fort somewhere
down South. He was a second lieutenant at the time, and had

been for many, many months, largely because he and his commanding officer didn't get on very well. The man and his wife also had a dog at their house—a young puppy who was in the puppy stage of chewing up her slippers and clothes. They had a small family joke, based on an old James Thurber cartoon, whereby she pretended to blame her *husband* for all the damage the puppy did to their belongings. (This is a pretty complicated story, but all dog stories are complicated.) Anyway, one Sunday morning their doorbell rang, the lieutenant went to the door and was astonished to discover that his commanding officer had brought his wife over for a surprise social call—their very first. The lieutenant welcomed them and poured some coffee. They were attempting small talk when the lieutenant's wife, unaware that there were callers, opened her bedroom door upstairs. "John!" she shouted down, "have you been chewing the seat out of my pajamas again?"

The man explained to me that he and his visitors just sat there, in absolute silence, for a good ten seconds—long enough for him to realize that the whole thing was too complex, too hopelessly scrambled and implausible, for him to attempt any explanation. In the end all three of them simply pretended that the interruption hadn't taken place at all. After a minute or two of strained conversation, the C.O. and his wife got up and left. A week later the man was abruptly transferred to another outfit and shipped overseas.

In general, I guess dog and owner have an easier time of it in the country or suburbs than in the city, simply because it is easier for them to be independent of each other. My wife, however, once owned an old English sheep dog who managed to upset the smooth calm life of an entire community. He was a suburban dog who lived on a crowded hillside near Boston. He was also a kleptomaniac. He first evidenced this weakness by systematically collecting the food pans of every dog in the neighborhood, bringing them home, and piling them up outside his own kitchen door. A few weeks later it began to appear that the local milkman had gone crazy. Every morning, instead of the usual two quarts of milk, my wife's mother would find a dozen or fifteen quarts piled up at the back door. A couple of days later the disease seemed to spread to the newsboy, who apparently was delivering everybody's *Boston Herald* to the same house. The milk company and the newsdealer were flooded with angry complaints, the delivery men were insulted and offered to quit, husbands blamed wives and mothers blamed children. After a week or so, of course, the culprit was discovered and was thereafter kept indoors in the morning. My wife's mother telephoned her apologies to everyone and tried to smooth ruffled feelings. "You know how dogs are," she said lamely. Nobody was particularly amused. I still remember the day of the first thaw that winter, when the snow on the road trickled away and revealed dozens of soggy newspapers and half frozen bottles of milk which the busy dog had dropped on his rounds.

Finally I come to Fred. All the other dogs I have dealt with here were largely blameless and their mishaps involuntary. Fred, on the other hand, was a plotter. He never made a move in his life which he hadn't carefully thought out. Every one of his twenty-odd consecutive losing bouts with porcupines was calculated; he simply had decided that he was capable of handling a porcupine and nobody was going to teach him better. He was on separate terms (largely indifferent) with everyone in his rather large household, and he never deviated. His major studies in life, along with porcupines, included sheep-herding, the cultivation of a gallant and entirely fraudulent limp, the art of drinking beer out of nearly empty bottles, and the fanning of a lifelong feud with his veterinarian.

I was there the day that Fred decided to Get the Vet. He was a pretty old dog by this time—a tremendous red dachshund whose entire muzzle and shoulders had turned white. I doubt that when I found him that morning lying inert and helpless beside the kitchen steps, he had yet formulated his entire complex plan, but he was working on it. In any case, I was pretty worried. My parents, who owned Fred, were away on a trip, the veterinarian was twenty-five miles away, and I was pretty sure, after a careful examination, that I had a dying dog on my hands. I called my brother and we both tried unsuccessfully to coax Fred onto his feet. Then we found a burlap bag, tenderly laid the animal on it, and used this improvised stretcher to carry him to the car. Fred's eyes rolled alarmingly and he let out a few brave groans as we laid him on the floor of the sedan.

He lay there without moving throughout the long trip to the vet's while I gently eased the car over the bumps and framed in my mind the sad telegram to my parents. When we got there, we unloaded our bundle and laid it gently on the floor of the vet's office. The doctor was unimpressed. He had been bitten several times during Fred's numerous porcupine-quill extractions and was a full partner in their feud. "Sick, huh," he said now without sympathy. He circled the prostrate dog warily. Suddenly he shouted, "Get up, Fred! You old faker."

Fred rolled his eyes but didn't move. This obviously impressed the vet. Gradually, as he took Fred's temperature and listened with his stethoscope, his skepticism vanished and was replaced with genuine sympathy. "I guess he's really begun to slow down," he said sadly. I remarked that the dog's shoulder had seemed terribly sore. The vet now got down on his hands and knees to examine the shoulder. This was the closest he had allowed himself to come to Fred's jaws, and Fred now saw his chance. With a tremendous roar he threw himself into the air and slashed at the doctor's arm. The vet snatched his hand back just in time, staggered backward, and landed on the floor. Fred, who had not moved a muscle for the previous three hours, scurried rapidly across the room and crawled under a chair, from where he let loose some growling curses over his bad luck in having missed his target.

The vet, just as angry at having let himself be taken in, picked himself up and made up a prescription for Fred's heart (which seemed strong enough to me) and we took our leave. When I opened the car door, Fred leaped easily up into the back seat. He sat there the whole way home, looking out the window and chuckling quietly to himself.

Fred is dead now, but I wish somehow I could pass him along to that sports columnist for a few days' visit. The man would find that his ego, instead of being enlarged, would rapidly show signs of wear, but I think he'd enjoy it just the same. Perhaps he would decide, as I have, that for a man, taking on a dog is just like taking on a wife and raising a family. On the surface, it is a senseless thing to do, since it quickly deprives you of a good portion of your freedom, mobility, pride, and independence. There are moments when you remember this, but most of the time you know that you just couldn't get along without such a pleasantly cluttered life. Maybe the sportswriter wouldn't feel this way, though. I understand he is also a bachelor.

daley's dorg wattle

W. T. GOODGE

"You can talk about yer sheep dorgs," said the man from
    Allan's Creek,
"But I know a dorg that simply knocked 'em bandy! —
Do whatever you would show him, and you'd hardly need
    to speak;
Owned by Daley, drover cove in Jackandandy.

"We was talkin' in the parlour, me and Daley, quiet like,
When a blow-fly starts a-buzzin' round the ceilin',
Up gets Daley, and he says to me, 'You wait a minute, Mike,
And I'll show you what a dorg he is at heelin'.'

"And an empty pickle-bottle was a-standin' on the shelf,
Daley takes it down and puts it on the table,
And he bets me drinks that blinded dorg would do it by
    himself —
And I didn't think as how as he was able!

"Well, he shows the dorg the bottle, and he points up to the fly,
And he shuts the door, and says to him — 'Now Wattle!'
And in less than fifteen seconds, spare me days, it ain't a lie,
That there dorg has got that inseck in the bottle."

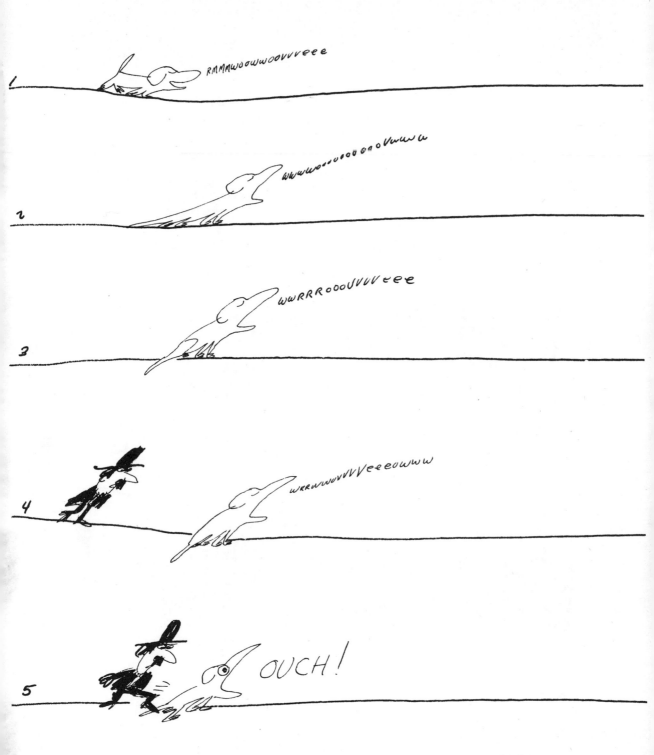

A. B. SENS

ROY McKIE

the swimming lesson

ARTHUR P. JACOBS

"Can't swim?" shouted Harrison, with such a sharp note of incredulity that several people looked out of windows in the houses opposite. "Why, bless my soul, *every* dog can swim. Some need more encouragement than others, that's all." He glanced appraisingly at Cæsar, who returned the look with interest. Having mutually sized each other up they decided to put the matter to the test.

My wife and I and Harrison accompanied Cæsar to the boating pond in the park, and on the way I pointed out to Harrison that he was attempting the impossible. I said I had tried many, many times to get Cæsar into the water, but it usually ended by the procedure being reversed. Harrison asked in superior tones how I set about it. I said I waited until Cæsar's attention was fully occupied elsewhere, then I crept up behind him and gave a sudden push. Harrison remarked that the method was crude and certainly unscientific. Any fool should know that an animal jumps sideways when pushed from behind. He said it was an instinctive reaction and that I deserved to have a ducking because of my inexcusable ignorance of such matters.

During our walk to the park Cæsar must have been surreptitiously inviting other dogs to come along, for by the time we reached the water's edge we found ourselves at the head of a procession which stretched for fifty yards or more behind us. It was a quiet, orderly procession—intent upon enjoying itself later on. I've known a crowd converging on a football ground to show similar signs of suppressed excitement.

Harrison said the great thing was to put the dog at ease; then it became sufficiently self-confident to jump in of its own accord. I pointed out that Cæsar always appeared to have self-confidence in over-abundance, but Harrison didn't hear—he was down on one knee beside Cæsar, whispering encouragement in his right ear. Apparently this tickled the beast, for after a moment it started to scratch itself, taking Harrison by surprise so that he toppled over backwards. As if they regarded this as a curtain-raiser all the other dogs moved forward into better positions around the pond. Their tongues lolled out expectantly and several of the more excitable ones set up a shrill yapping.

Cæsar finished scratching, investigated the recumbent Harrison, and after sniffing at him for a second or two blew in his face. Harrison struggled into an upright position, shooed away a dozen or more of the nearest spectators, and having patted Cæsar to show he bore him no ill-will told him to sit down. Cæsar sat down and winked at the other dogs; then he put his face to the sky and howled. Cæsar's howling wasn't a pretty sound, and Harrison turned around to ask me sharply if the dog were ill. I said no he wasn't ill, he always made that noise when he wanted to play. Harrison said that a bit of discipline might do Cæsar a lot of good; then he went down on one knee again and all the dogs assumed expressions of pleasurable anticipation.

Harrison put one arm around Cæsar and pointed with his other to the distant shore opposite. He appeared to be exhorting the animal to deeds of heroism by making an impassioned recital of some ancient saga. Cæsar suddenly jumped to his feet, backed from under Harrison's caressing touch and led

a yelling cohort of canine friends around the edge of the pond
on a furious sortie—the main purpose of which was to take
a look at the enemy Harrison had told them lurked on the far
side. To save himself from pitching into the water Harrison
flung out his other hand and thereby made unexpected and
violent contact with a passing mongrel of immense proportions,
who first gave a yelp of surprise and then made a wide circle
around him, glaring back over its shoulder every few steps
and hurling a mixture of threats and derision in his direction.

By the time Harrison had risen to his feet again Cæsar and
his company of desperadoes had completed the circuit of the
pond and were now clustered around their human friend,
noisily pointing out to him that he had been in error in sup-
posing there to be anything wrong over yonder.

Harrison discouraged a few of the more enthusiastic animals
with his foot, and then singled Cæsar out from among the
crowd pressing so thickly about him. Cæsar sat down again
and the others sorted themselves out, with their attention
divided equally between Harrison and a private fight which
suddenly started immediately behind him. Harrison waved
his walking-stick like a conductor of a symphony orchestra, the
individual performers of which had gone completely mad. Dogs
flew from him on all sides, and when quiet was finally restored
only six others besides Cæsar remained. All the survivors sat
on their haunches and licked their lips in an effort to appear
quite at ease.

Then, very gently, Harrison placed the stick in Cæsar's
mouth. Cæsar looked surprised at this and wagged his tail. He
had half expected a whack over the head, and Thor having
offered him this thunderbolt instead successfully calmed his
doggy fears. Harrison removed the stick, backed a few paces
and put it down on the ground; then he called Cæsar and
told him to pick it up. After this had been repeated several
times Cæsar began to look as though Harrison had taken leave
of his senses—but he cheerfully continued to oblige all the

same. Until, that is, Harrison snatched away the stick from under his nose and hurled it across the pond to the far bank. Cæsar at once let out a bark of consternation, which effectively summoned the remaining dogs to his side, then led them off *around* the pond once more.

This time the mass idea seemed to approximate more to the running of a friendly race than the making of a warlike sortie. Two dogs soon gained the lead, and when the whole company reached the other side Cæsar could do no better than hold grimly on to third place. A Manchester terrier seized hold of Harrison's stick, swung around happily and pushed the end of it into a companion's face, then made off at a brisk pace towards the distant gates. Most of the other dogs gave up the chase after a minute or two, each making its separate way homewards. The general feeling seemed to be that a good time had been had by all and there was little merit in flogging a dead horse—Harrison couldn't reasonably be expected to provide any more fun. But they didn't know Harrison.

Within a quarter of an hour he had not only retrieved his stick but was once more down on his knees at Cæsar's side by the edge of the water. He tried placing the stick a number of times in Cæsar's mouth, and then, with much bravado, threw it into the middle of the pond. Cæsar first looked shocked— then anxious. He trotted around the edge several times in a helpless kind of way, then finally rushed off howling as though the devil were after him.

It took us some time to convince Harrison that if his stick really were valuable he had better wade in after it. We finally achieved success by instilling confidence into him. As the parkkeeper said when we fetched him along, the pond was an artificial one with a good concrete bottom, and in no place was it more than a foot deep. He said it had been kept shallow on purpose. In summer the kids could paddle, and the dogs weren't tempted to go swimming in it as they would have been if the water was any deeper.

wiles's dog

"It's me, boy! I've come back!"

"Good grief! You're not jealous?"

once bitten

from *Next to Oddliness*

PAUL JENNINGS

Perhaps one of the reasons why talking to dogs has reached, in the twentieth century, a degree of conviction never known before is that man instinctively knows himself to be neither the highest nor the lowest intelligence in the universe; and now that the broodingness has gone out of our earth and the voice of Pan is silent, there is an even greater poignancy in the curious intelligence, so like and so unlike our own, that looks out of the eyes of dogs, bringing a hint of the Other, of the vast wordless articulation of Nature, into the most sterile blocks of flats.

Talking to dogs is one of the few acts of faith still made nowadays. "Come along, darling, we must get back in case the plumber comes," I heard a woman say to her dog. She was an intelligent-looking woman, who would, presumably, have admitted that the concept "plumber" or even merely the overtones of the word "darling," are far beyond a dog's comprehension. Yet she sent out this human message, not simply as an absurd subjective statement in the wind—a *mad* statement; she made an unquestioned act of faith, that she was somehow communicating with that subfusc limbo of the intelligence where animals have their being.

For myself, I am rarely capable of this act of faith. I like dogs, I have had dogs myself, but there is something in me that stops me from talking about plumbers to them; and they know it. Their knowing it does not necessarily make them dislike me in the way that some creatures—bees, for instance—dislike me (I like bees, too. I talk romantically about the Fourth Georgic. But when friends show me their bees they simply sting my head. Some fearful, Martian rumour of cold, irrational hate goes round the hive. Fall in the guard. It's Jennings, the hive-wrecker, the bee-hater. Die for the Fatherland. Sting his head) . No, dogs simply behave *differently* towards me.

Often they get hysterical. I go to a party at a house where they have a rather soppy boxer, who jumps up at each new arrival. But he quietens down, and when we start playing an acting game he remains perfectly quiet until it is my turn. Then he gets hysterical. He shadow-boxes with me, I have to laugh him off, as if he were a drunken friend whom I wished to quieten without offending. He knows I am worried about this act of faith, he is trying shock tactics from his side.

Of course, dogs (and bees) are in much more direct contact with the world-store of love and hate than we are, with our clouds of bodiless words, and there are dramatic, critical moments when even I make this act of faith. The other day, lunching in a pub, I asked for the telephone and I was directed to the end of a brown corridor; and there was an awful Alsatian, baring its teeth at me (I'd like to see anybody breathe down *its* nose to win its confidence) . I heard myself saying, "It's all right, boy, I'm only telephoning." *Boy*, I said *boy*. True, I spoke partly for the benefit of the barmaid who was passing with a tray, hoping to be drawn into the obviously peaceful relationship between her and this terrible dog—but also partly to the dog itself, as an act of faith.

It is always more confusing when human beings are involved as well. I was once walking in Kensington Gardens, in that slack week-day late afternoon when the earth gives off a dull

light from inside, and a man feels curiously alien, oppressed
by the heavy, quiescent life-force of women, and children out
of school, and dogs. There was a commotion by the Round
Pond, caused by a fight between a boxer and a spaniel. The
boxer had the spaniel by the neck and was scientifically trying
to drown it. I had read in a dog-lovers' magazine that most
people just grin foolishly at a dog-fight, a legacy from the bear-
baiting and cock-fighting days, or else they sadistically throw
pepper or use a stick, whereas the correct way is to hold the
uppermost dog by tail and collar and "turn it gently through
180 degrees."

I tried this on the boxer and it turned its head briefly and
bit two fingers to the bone. So I got a cane from a boy who
was fishing and hit it very hard. It immediately let go of the
spaniel and walked away, with a small sigh.

Quite a large and sympathetic crowd gathered and vocally
expressed solicitude over the wound, and various plans of
assistance were being made while I, unspoken to, was walking
away. It wasn't my wound they were discussing, but the spaniel's.

GIOVANNETTI

SIGGS

SYVERSON

"I often wonder what they see in each other."

VIRGIL PARTCH (VIP)

"Ferguson, I'd like a word with you."

DUMAS

the dog at the german inn

from *Three Men on the Bummel*

JEROME K. JEROME

It was a comfortable little restaurant, where they cooked well.
We stopped there for a couple of hours, and dried ourselves
and fed ourselves, and talked about the view; and just before
we left an incident occurred that shows how much more
stirring in this world are the influences of evil compared with
those of good.

A traveller entered. He seemed a careworn man. He carried
a brick in his hand, tied to a piece of rope. He entered nervously and hurriedly, closed the door carefully behind him,
saw to it that it was fastened, peered out of the window long
and earnestly, and then, with a sigh of relief, laid his brick
upon the bench beside him and called for food and drink.

There was something mysterious about the whole affair. One
wondered what he was going to do with the brick, why he
had closed the door so carefully, why he had looked so anxiously from the window; but his aspect was too wretched to
invite conversation, and we forebore, therefore, to ask him
questions. As he ate and drank he grew more cheerful, sighed
less often. Later he stretched his legs, lit an evil-smelling cigar,
and puffed in calm contentment.

Then it happened. It happened too suddenly for any detailed explanation of the thing to be possible. I recollect a Fräulein entering the room from the kitchen with a pan in her hand. I saw her cross to the outer door. The next moment the whole room was in an uproar. One was reminded of those pantomime transformation scenes where, from among floating clouds, slow music, waving flowers, and reclining fairies, one is suddenly transported into the midst of shouting policemen tumbling over yelling babies, swells fighting pantaloons, sausages and harlequins, buttered slides and clowns. As the Fräulein of the pan touched the door it flew open, as though all the spirits of sin had been pressed against it, waiting. Two pigs and a chicken rushed into the room; a cat that had been sleeping on a beer barrel spluttered into fiery life. The Fräulein threw her pan into the air and lay down on the floor. The gentleman with the brick sprang to his feet, upsetting the table before him with everything upon it.

One looked to see the cause of the disaster; one discovered
it at once in the person of a mongrel terrier with pointed ears
and a squirrel's tail. The landlord rushed out from another
door, and attempted to kick him out of the room. Instead,
he kicked one of the pigs, the fatter of the two. It was a vig-
orous, well-planted kick, and the pig got the whole of it, none
of it was wasted. One felt sorry for the poor animal; but no
amount of sorrow anyone else might feel for him could com-
pare with the sorrow he felt for himself. He stopped running
about; he sat down in the middle of the room, and appealed
to the solar system generally to observe the unjust thing that
had come upon him. They must have heard this complaint in
the valleys round about, and have wondered what upheaval
of nature was taking place among the hills.

As for the hen it scuttled, screaming, every way at once. It
was a marvellous bird; it seemed to be able to run up a straight
wall quite easily; and it and the cat between them fetched
down most everything that was not already on the floor. In
less than forty seconds there were nine people in that room,
all trying to kick one dog. Possibly, now and again, one or
another may have succeeded, for occasionally the dog would
stop barking in order to howl. But it did not discourage him.
Everything has to be paid for, he evidently argued, even a pig
and chicken hunt; and, on the whole, the game was worth it.

Besides, he had the satisfaction of observing that, for every
kick he received, most other living things in the room got two.
As for the unfortunate pig—the stationary one, the one that
still sat lamenting in the centre of the room—he must have
averaged a steady four. Trying to kick this dog was like playing football with a ball that was never there—not when you
went to kick it, but after you had started to kick it, and had
gone too far to stop yourself, so that the kick had to go on in
any case, your only hope being that your foot would find something or another solid to stop it, and so save you from sitting

down on the floor noisily and completely. When anybody did
kick the dog it was by pure accident, when they were not expecting to kick him; and, generally speaking, this took them so
unawares that, after kicking him, they fell over him. And everybody, every half-minute, would be certain to fall over the pig
—the sitting pig, the one incapable of getting out of anybody's
way.

How long the scrimmage might have lasted it is impossible
to say. It was ended by the judgement of George. For a while
he had been seeking to catch, not the dog but the remaining
pig, the one still capable of activity. Cornering it at last, he
persuaded it to cease running round and round the room, and
instead to take a spin outside. It shot through the door with
one long wail.

We always desire the thing we have not. One pig, a chicken,
nine people, and a cat, there was nothing in that dog's opinion
compared with the quarry that was disappearing. Unwisely,
he darted after it, and George closed the door on him and shot
the bolt.

Then the landlord stood up and surveyed all the things that
were lying on the floor.

"That's a playful dog of yours," said he to the man who
had come in with the brick.

"He's not my dog," replied the man sullenly.

"Whose dog is it then?" said the landlord.

"I don't know whose dog it is," answered the man.

"That won't do for me, you know," said the landlord, picking up a picture of the German Emperor, and wiping beer
from it with his sleeve.

"I know it won't," replied the man. "I never expected it
would. I'm tired of telling people it isn't my dog. They none
of them believe me."

"What do you want to go about with him for, if he's not
your dog?" said the landlord. "What's the attraction about
him?"

"I don't go about with him," replied the man; "he goes about with me. He picked me up this morning at ten o'clock, and he won't leave me. I thought I had got rid of him when I came in here. I left him busy killing a duck more than a quarter of an hour away. I'll have to pay for that, I expect, on my way back."

"Have you tried throwing stones at him?" asked Harris.

"Have I tried throwing stones at him!" replied the man contemptuously. "I've been throwing stones at him till my arm aches with throwing stones; and he thinks it's a game, and brings them back to me. I've been carrying this beastly brick about with me for over an hour, in the hope of being able to drown him, but he never comes near enough for me to get hold of him. He just sits six inches out of reach with his mouth open and looks at me."

"It's the funniest story I've heard for a long while," said the landlord.

"Glad it amuses somebody," said the man.

We left him helping the landlord to pick up the broken things and went our way. A dozen yards outside the doorway the faithful animal was waiting for his friend. He looked tired but contented.

Illustrated by L. Raven Hill

thelwell's dogs

The Show Dog

The Messenger Dog

The Lap Dog

The Gun Dog

The Guard Dog

The Stray Dog

ffolkes's dogs

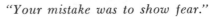

"Your mistake was to show fear."

"Mine has moist eyes, a straggly mustache, and answers to the name of Willoughby."

"He's past his best."

"Very funny."

the dog who paid cash

from *The Autobiography of Will Rogers*

WILL ROGERS

While I didn't have anything else to do, I got to watching an
old spotted dog. He was just an ordinary dog, but when I
looked at him close, he was alert and friendly with everyone.
Got to inquiring around and found out he'd been bumped off
a freight train and seemed to have no owner. He made himself at home and started right in business. When a crowd of
cowboys would go into a saloon, he would follow 'em in and
begin entertaining. He could do all kinds of tricks—turn somersaults, lay down and roll over, sit up on his hind feet, and
such like.

He would always rush to the door and shake hands with
all the newcomers. The boys would lay a coin on his nose, and
he'd toss it high in the air and catch it in his mouth and pretend to swallow it. But you could bet your life he didn't swallow it—he stuck it in one side of his lip and when he got a
lip full of money, he'd dash out the back door and disappear
for a few minutes. What he had really done was hide his money.
As soon as he worked one saloon, he would pull out and go to
another place.

I got to thinking while watching this old dog, how much
smarter he is than me. Here I am out of a job five hundred
miles from home and setting around and can't find a thing to

do, and this old dog hops off a train and starts right in making money, hand over fist.

Me and some boys around town tried to locate his hidden treasure but this old dog was too slick for us. He never fooled away no time on three or four of us boys that was looking for work. He seemed to know we was broke, but he was very friendly. As he was passing along by me, he'd wag his tail and kinda wink. I musta looked hungry and forlorn. I think he wanted to buy me a meal.

When times was dull and he got hungry, he would mysteriously disappear. Pretty soon he'd show up at a butcher shop with a dime in his mouth and lay it on the counter and the butcher would give him a piece of steak or a bone. He always paid for what he got in the line of grub. Pretty soon he seemed to get tired of the town, and one morning he was gone. A railroad man told us later that he seen the same dog in Trinidad, Colorado.

"For Heaven's sake, why don't you go outdoors and trace something?"

JAMES THURBER

index

about the editor

WILLIAM COLE has edited many anthologies, including *Beastly Boys and Ghastly Girls*, *The Birds and the Beasts Were There*, *Poems for Seasons and Celebrations*, *I Went to the Animal Fair*, and *Humorous Poetry for Children*. He is also the editor of several anthologies for adults, among them *The Fireside Book of Humorous Poetry* and *The Classic Cartoons*. Reading and the study of humor are two of his favorite pastimes. He is a native New Yorker and has two children.